C-3

D0962003

C-3

9/66

AMERICAN
HEROES
ALL

AMERICAN HEROES ALL

*Stories of our servicemen in action
in the wars of the United States from
the American Revolution to Korea*

Selected by Albert B. Tibbets

Little, Brown
and Company
Boston   Toronto

ACKNOWLEDGMENTS

For permission to reprint copyrighted material the following acknowl-
edgments are gratefully made:

To James Warner Bellah for his stories "The Secret of the Seven
Days" and "Fear."

To The Bobbs-Merrill Company, Inc., for "Battle of New Orleans"
from *The Cavalier of Tennessee* by Meredith Nicholson, copyright 1928
by The Bobbs-Merrill Company, Inc., R. 1955 by Meredith Nicholson,
Jr. Reprinted by permission of the publishers.

To The John Day Company, Inc., and the author's agents Littauer
and Wilkinson for "Reluctant Hero" from *Combat Stories of World
War II and Korea* by William Chamberlain, copyright © 1961 by The
Curtis Publishing Company, copyright © 1964 by William Chamber-
lain. And for "Star Over Korea" from *More Combat Stories of World
War II and Korea* by William Chamberlain, copyyright © 1952 by
The Curtis Publishing Company, copyright © 1962 by William Cham-

In Appreciation

I am deeply grateful to the following for their help on this book:

To Mrs. Kay Rainey Gray, press correspondent, United Nations, New York;

To Anne Izard and Julia Losinski, Westchester County, New York, Library System;

To Mrs. Elizabeth Martin, reference librarian, Danbury, Connecticut, Public Library;

To Charles and Edward O'Malley, O'Malley's Book Store, New York City, who were indefatigable in finding out-of-print books for me;

To Emile C. Schurmacher, who made available to me his personal and comprehensive reference file;

To my two editors: Therese Doumenjou, editor-in-chief of the Junior Literary Guild; and Helen Jones, editor of books for young people, Little, Brown and Company;

And to my wife, Helen Ferris, who is incompetent as a proofreader but of high excellence in the realm of ideas.

A. B. T.

In Appreciation

For Freedom

As I chose these stories for you, I found myself beside those brave young Americans of other days. I was with the troops of General Marion when they captured the belfries of Georgetown to ring in the Fourth of July. I was in the Civil War balloon basket with Davin Ancrum when he went aloft to make a map of the enemy's whereabouts. I was with the Marines in the First World War when they adopted a stray dog and named her "Verdun Belle." And I was with Eddie Norton as he endured a lonely wait off the shores of Korea.

And I knew that General Marion's men, making the perilous raids from their hiding places in the swamps, had no idea of a United States of America stretching from the Atlantic Ocean to the Pacific. Nor did the hundreds of the other young men in the American Colonies who so gallantly fought in the American Revolution. They went into combat because they were determined to protect the right to live their own kind of life, and so that their families and friends might do the same. The banner of their spirit was bright with the words: "For Freedom." The same banner flew high above American servicemen in the wars that followed fought by the United States. Stories about them, too, are in this book.

So deeply did Americans of the more recent yesterdays and we of today cherish that freedom that we wished to see it become a reality for all the world. We willingly joined people of other countries and nations in bringing this about. Because of this, our country sent its young men into the First World War and then into the Second.

But all the while, we were sure that a better way than war could be found for settling the disagreements between countries. The League of Nations had that goal and many of us campaigned for it. But too many others doubted that it could be made to work.

And then, following the Second World War, the United Nations was organized, and today countless men and women in the United States and around the world are confident that the U.N. will achieve its goal — peace on earth and goodwill among all nations.

ALBERT B. TIBBETS

Contents

IN THE AMERICAN REVOLUTION

1776-1783

From

Commander-in-Chief George Washington

George Washington became a major in the Colonial Army before he was twenty-one years of age. In the American Revolution, he was promoted to general, then commander-in-chief of the Continental Army. To him, each soldier, each serviceman was his friend, a feeling he warmly conveyed to his officers in his farewell to them in Fraunces' Tavern, New York, on September 17, 1783:

"With a heart full of gratitude, I take leave of you. And I most devoutly wish that your latter days may be as prosperous and happy as your former ones have been glorious and honorable."

Bells of Freedom

by Paschal N. Strong

Colonel Tarleton didn't know who I was, of course, or I wouldn't have been his favorite stableboy. He'd have hanged me, most likely. He didn't know that his redcoats, after they captured Charleston, had burned my folks' place upriver. But mostly he didn't know that my Pa was in the swamps with General Francis Marion.

The Swamp Fox, as Colonel Tarleton called him, didn't have any troops to speak of. But he'd hide in the swamps and sometimes send out a signal for two or three dozen men to join him with their horses. Then they'd dash out to nip Tarleton here, and slice him there, and then fade back into the swamps again.

General Marion needed eyes everywhere and he had them. Colonel Tarleton would be mighty surprised if he knew I was one of them. I guess he figured nobody as skinny and freckled as I was

could bother his cavalry troopers much. He had
taken a liking to me when his horse got loose one
night and I had found it and brought it back to him.
He'd be right surprised if he knew I was the one
who untethered it to begin with. Anyway, he liked
me the same way he liked his hound dogs — something he could pet when he felt good, and kick when
he got mad. But I didn't forget the sorrow he had
brought to Charleston. General Marion didn't send
me there to forget.

That's why I listened sharp when a captain and
a major rode into the stables from Georgetown, up
the coast. Tarleton was about to go for his morning
ride, and I had just brought around his big black
charger.

The captain and the major dismounted and I
held their horses while they talked.

"The Fox is coming out of the swamp," said the
major.

"Are you sure?" Tarleton demanded.

"Positive," said the captain. "I have a Loyalist
farmer who sometimes rides with Marion. He
brings me news. There's a plan afoot for a rebel
demonstration on the Fourth of July."

"Why the Fourth of July?" asked Tarleton.

"Have you forgotten, sir? That's the fourth anniversary of the signing of their rebellious document, the Declaration of Independence."

Tarleton laughed. "There'll never be another celebration of that day. We have Carolina at our feet, and soon Cornwallis will bring Washington's ragged mob to heel. But come, sir, tell me more of the Fox."

"He knows he must do something spectacular to keep alive the flame of rebellion. He has sent out word to all the towns and villages that the bells shall ring on the Fourth of July — even though we station troops in every belfry."

Tarleton's face hardened. "We'll know how to handle that. Belfries make good gallows for rebels. But you said Marion was coming out of the swamp."

"Aye, sir, that he is. He plans to enter Georgetown with his men, scatter our troops there and personally ring the bells. He was born thereabouts, I believe. He hopes to make those bells the symbol of defiance on Independence Day."

"I'll make it another symbol!" muttered Tarleton. "Who is this Loyalist farmer who brought you the news?"

"His name is Blackshear. He serves us while we pay him."

"Then pay him well — and send him back to the swamp. We must know more, so we can set a trap."

The major smiled in anticipation. "You will be there, sir?"

"Aye," laughed Tarleton. "I shall be there with enough troops to skin the Fox. But no word of this to anyone."

The captain looked hard at me, but Tarleton laughed. "The boy has proved his loyalty to the King's shilling. Now come to my quarters, and we will lay our plans. There is but a week until the Fourth." He nodded curtly to me. "Lead Black Star round the market place for exercise," he ordered.

But I figured Black Star needed more exercise than that; so I took him to the fish wharves and bought a mackerel for the stable mess. After I talked to Old Jock, the fisherman, he reckoned he'd go upriver that afternoon, to where the pine swamps come down to the tidewater.

We stableboys were mighty fond of fish, and I had to go back to the fish wharves the next day. Old Jock took a long time to find just the right mackerel and wrap it up.

"This 'un's too small," he said. "How's Tarleton going to Georgetown?"

"By ship. He figures if he takes his troops overland, Marion will find out."

"Now here's a right smart mackerel. What ship?"

"The *Maid O' Malone* — that West Indies merchantman tied up near the Battery. There's no cannon aboard her. She's due to leave anyway on the morning tide of July second. Tarleton will load his troops secretly the night before."

"Now here's one just the right size. Maybe Tarleton ain't so smart. He'll get to Georgetown Bay all right, but like as not he'll run into the night calm there."

"He thought of that. He's sent word to Georgetown to have a lot of bateaux ready with a pilot. They're to meet him down bay at midnight and tow him in."

"Well, well! Now here's your fish."

I stuck the mackerel in the saddlebag. "General Marion will be careful about Blackshear — and he won't try to ring the bells at Georgetown, will he? Tarleton is taking the three hundred troopers. I never saw the general with more'n seventy men at any one time."

"The gin'ral figures the Fourth o' July is a kinda special day," grunted Old Jock. "He don't want the people to fergit it."

As I rode back, I worried. I couldn't forget my Pa was with the general, everywhere he went. I looked at the *Maid O' Malone* down by the Battery and worried some more.

A pack of small boys threw stones at me as I approached Tarleton's quarters. "Freckle-faced Tory!" they shouted. It sort of hurt, especially as I had to call 'em names, too.

As time went by, my worry grew. On the first of July a Georgetown trooper came in. He had a farmer with him — Blackshear. Tarleton took Blackshear into his quarters for a long talk. Usually I could manage to hear something, but this time I couldn't. When they came out, Tarleton looked mighty pleased.

"Do you think Black Star can stand a sea trip?" he asked me.

My heart jumped. If he was taking Black Star, I'd go too. "Yes, sir," I said, so fast that Tarleton laughed.

"A lot you know about it, boy. But tell the captain of the *Maid O' Malone* to load him aboard tonight. You come along and look to his fodder."

I knew why Tarleton wanted Black Star. He wanted to prance around Georgetown on the charger after he had captured the Swamp Fox.

Suppose General Marion hadn't got my warning about Blackshear. He'd be walking right into the trap!

That afternoon Old Jock came around to peddle

fish. "The bells will ring —" he whispered to me — "everywhere!"

"In Georgetown, too?" I asked.

"Aye, in Georgetown."

I told him about Blackshear's visit. He shook his head but said nothing.

A dying moon rose over the bay when we loaded that night, and the town was as quiet as black velvet. The troops came aboard in small groups, like ghosts. Black Star and I shared a stall in the ship's waist. There was just enough breeze to keep the sails billowed out as we dropped down the bay. When we reached the open sea, Tarleton came on deck and gave Black Star a bit of sugar.

"Keep the stall clean," he told me. "It'll be a fine place to keep the Swamp Fox when we bring him back."

I was glad he couldn't see my face in the dark.

All that day and the next we stood off the coast, just out of sight of Georgetown Bay. The troopers were allowed on the deck, and my heart was heavy as I counted them. They were talking brave talk of what they'd do to the Swamp Fox when they got ashore. I kept my ears open and learned of Tarleton's plans, but there was no way to get word to Old Jock.

Tarleton had learned from Blackshear that General Marion was going to slip into Georgetown an hour after daybreak on the Fourth. He would come in by the Old Plank Road, overcome the small red-coat garrison, and give the people a rousing celebration of Independence Day. Tarleton's plan was to reach town an hour ahead of Marion and conceal his three hundred troopers. He would let the town's outposts be overrun by Marion; and then, when the Fox and his men galloped into town, he would spring the trap and capture them. I was so worried I could hardly care for Black Star.

On the evening of the third, we picked up the night breeze and ghosted into Georgetown Bay. The breeze left us near midnight, and the lookouts strained their eyes for the signal lights of the bateaux that were to meet us and pull us in. One by one the lights of Georgetown went out; and there we were, drifting in with the rising tide.

Then a light shone out of the darkness and we heard a hail. I was on the forecastle, and finally I made out a half-dozen large bateaux. Six men with long oars sat in each of them. We took one of the men aboard, and our sailors passed a hawser down to the bateaux. Soon they were towing our large ship.

Tarleton and the captain came up to the fore-castle, to talk to the stranger. "Is there a good pilot in the lead boat?" asked the captain. "I don't want to ground on the sand bars."

"Aye, sir, that there is," replied the newcomer.

I gripped the rail to keep from shouting out. Only one man in the world had that voice. I slowly turned around to look at my Pa, and for a second our eyes met.

"If things suit ye, I'll slide down the hawser and get back to my oar," Pa said to the captain.

"Get back. But mind you men stay clear of the sand bars."

As my Pa slipped by me, he gave me an elbow in the ribs; then he went down the hawser, hand over hand. My thoughts spun round like squirrels in a cage. If Pa was up ahead in those boats, General Marion must be there, too. And *they* were towing Tarleton into Georgetown!

An hour, two hours, three hours went by. The tide was ebbing now, but the town was close. I heard the call of a sentry across the quiet night. Then I heard the soft crunch of keel against the sand. We were on a sand bar — and the tide was falling!

Shouts of dismay rose from the ship. But I was going to be with Marion this Fourth of July! I dived overboard and struck out for the nearest boat. "Wait for me!" I shouted. Soon a man pulled me on board the bateau, and I heard my Pa chuckling in the dark.

"I thought you might come. But the General doesn't like it. You're of more value with Tarleton."

Yes, sir, there was General Marion right next to me. And that wasn't all. In the bottom of the boat, gagged and trussed were six redcoats. They looked as mad as roosters with wet feathers.

"Lines all clear, Gin'ral," someone said.

"Flash the signal forward," said the General, and my Pa pulled a black cloth from a lantern and waved the light.

"Now, pull for your lives," ordered General Marion. "When Tarleton finds what is up, he'll signal the town."

Our men pulled until I thought the oars would break. The men in the other bateaux did the same, and the shouting and clamor of the ship sounded fainter and fainter. Then a musketry volley cracked the night and I ducked.

Another volley, and another. "That's the alarm," said General Marion. "The redcoat garrison at Georgetown doesn't know what's happened, but they're being alerted. We may have fireworks before our bell ringing, lads."

He turned to me. "How many small boats on the ship?"

"Just a couple of gigs and a longboat for the crew, sir."

"Good. They can't send enough soldiers ashore at one time to bother us. You did good work, boy."

"I was worried, sir. Blackshear came to Charleston and —"

"I know. He told Tarleton my plans. Only, they weren't my *real* plans. He didn't know them. Harkee, son. There's a touch of dawn in the east. There'll be glory in the sky today — and such sounds as will ring forth through America."

Cree-unk! went the oarlocks. *Spur-lash!* went the oars. And on went the bateaux as the darkness turned into light. General Marion conferred with my Pa.

"We've captured two dozen of their garrison. There are two dozen more at their outposts. So there are just a dozen left in the town."

"I figure likewise. If our mounted men engage the outposts as you plan —"

"They will. As soon as they hear the bells." He thought a moment. "We'll go straight to the landing. If the redcoats there stand for a fight, we'll rush them."

"Just show your face, General, and you'll see their heels."

"I hope so. I want no bloodshed today. Pull, men. I want our boat to be the first to touch!"

As we edged into the lead, there was enough light to see the wharves and the river street. I saw two or three soldiers running and heard a drum sending out a rolling tattoo. Shutters opened, and curious citizens looked out. I picked up a musket from one of the bound redcoats and looked to the priming. If there was fighting, I could shoot with the best.

Now we were but a hundred yards from the landing. A dozen British soldiers were milling around in confusion. I guess they didn't quite know who we were or what had happened.

Fifty yards from shore. Twenty-five! Now each of us braced for the grounding, and prepared to rush the redcoats. General Marion stood up in the bow of the bateau and flung away the cloak that hid his uniform.

"It's the Swamp Fox!" shouted a redcoat. No more was needed. As we leaped ashore, the soldiers fled.

"To the belfry with me, boy!" shouted Marion. "You shall join us in ringing the bells."

The town hall was a scant hundred yards away. The door was locked, but my Pa and I smashed it with our muskets. General Marion led the way up the wooden steps to the belfry, and as he seized the rope, he handed me its end.

"Pull with me, boy! Sound in the Fourth of July!"

We pulled and pulled; and the great bell swung back and forth, sending out peals of sound that could have wakened the dead. I glanced down the bay. Tarleton's great ship stood motionless, her limp sails serving only to catch the glow of the rising sun.

"Ring, boy, ring!" shouted Marion. "Ring for liberty and freedom!"

We rang until my arms ached. And in between the great tones of the bell, I heard other bells come to life. Soon the people were assembled outside the town hall, and their cheers drowned out even the sound of the bells.

But it seemed to me I didn't see just the people of Georgetown. It seemed to me I saw all the people, up and down the country. They were waving and cheering this Fourth of July because somehow they knew they were going to be free. They just knew they were, that was all.

George Washington at Trenton

by Sonia Daugherty

Two sentries, in tattered uniforms, were talking in low voices in the entry of the fieldstone farmhouse.

"I guess he knows we're beaten." The younger of the two men nodded toward the large room where George Washington was walking up and down, his head bent low on his chest.

"You're wrong, Bill," exclaimed the older man. " 'Don't talk of yesterday; talk of tomorrow.' That's what he said to us after Germantown. He'll find a way —"

"You're a bookish man, Nat, you can talk. I'm practical. Facts is facts. We've been beaten all the way from New York across Westchester and up across New Jersey. And we didn't believe we were licked." Bill stooped down to wrap the rags around his bare feet. "We thought we'd sure trap the redcoats at Germantown." He jerked the rag up around his ankles with an angry frown. "They licked us again. We lost half our men at Germantown."

At this moment, the outside door was pulled open. A sharp gust of wind freshened the stale air for a moment. Young Hamilton entered hurriedly and banged the door shut. He had no overcoat, and his nose was blue with cold. He glanced at the sentries, received their salute with a haughty gesture, and went into the large, low-ceilinged room to whisper with Washington.

"I guess something's up," Nat leaned over to mumble to Bill. "I feel it in my bones."

"All I can feel is the wind down my back." Bill shivered and wriggled his frostbitten fingers to take the numbness out.

The outside door opened again. General Greene entered, letting in another draft of wind. The sentry stood at attention and saluted. General Greene, a tall, handsome man, his uniform stained with blood and smears of mud, returned the salute with a preoccupied air, walked swiftly into the large room, and laid a penciled chart on the table.

Washington leaned forward to examine the chart, and Hamilton unrolled a map and laid it beside the chart. The word "attack" spoken in a low voice reached Nat in the entry. Nat glanced anxiously at

Bill to see if he had heard. But Bill, busy with his thoughts, was paying no attention.

"The morale of the men is poor; in fact, it is very bad," said General Greene in a low voice. "I'm afraid there'll be many deserters when the men find out we're planning to attack Trenton on Christmas Day."

"A few good floggings would put an end to deserting," said young Hamilton smartly.

"I hope it won't come to that." Washington sighed and went over to the window to look out at the bleak New Jersey hills, coated in snow. If only Congress would remember that his men needed boots and that an army had to eat, he was thinking sadly.

Nat tried to catch a hint of what the officers were talking about in the large room, but their voices were so low he could only guess at a word now and then. He felt sure they were planning something important. He looked at Bill's red, unhappy face and shook his head sadly. Bill was very young.

"The generals told us we'd be celebrating Christmas in Philadelphia," said Bill, half to himself, half to Nat. "But Congress is smart. They know the redcoats'll take Philadelphia and they got themselves off to Baltimore. They're safe, and we're cooped up here in this valley, eating frozen potatoes, and glad to get even that." Bill spat onto the dusty floor.

"The redcoats haven't got Philadelphia yet," said Nat and began to whistle "Yankee Doodle."

General Washington turned from the window and glanced through the half-open door at his sentry. A shadow of a smile flickered into his tired eyes. "There's spirit in our men yet," he said softly. "But only a quick victory now can save our revolution."

General Greene studied the map as if he didn't know it by heart. "A surprise attack is our chief hope for success," he said thoughtfully.

"Some of the generals are of the opinion that we would have a better chance in the spring. We'd have more men," broke in Hamilton.

"By spring it would be all over with us." Washington spoke little above a whisper, but there was a determined ring in his voice and a flare of fire in his gray eyes. "We attack Trenton on the night of Christmas Day."

He leaned over the table and began to explain his plan: "Putnam and his men will come up from Philadelphia. Ewing and his men will cross near Trenton and join us before we cross the river. Glover's Marblehead fishermen will man the boats."

General Greene pulled a small, much-handled pamphlet from his pocket and began to read aloud — " 'These are the times that try men's souls . . .' "

" 'Try men's souls,' yes!" said Washington, taking

the pamphlet to page it in silence for a while. "Our men should read this pamphlet," he said, handing it back to General Greene. "We need what Thomas Paine has written here." Washington spoke slowly and with deliberation. He no longer looked harassed and tired. "I see that Paine calls this pamphlet *The Crisis*. His pamphlet *Common Sense* worked a powerful change in the minds of many men at the time when we were not certain of the revolution. This is the worst crisis we've ever had since then."

"Yes, Howe thinks we're finished, and Cornwallis is sending his baggage to New York to ship to England," said General Greene.

"Colonel Rahl and his Hessians are making great preparations for Christmas. They're boasting that we're done and finished for good. All the Tories in Trenton are planning parties for them." Hamilton said this with a smile, as if he were telling a joke.

"They'll discover they are mistaken," said Washington walking up and down, a frown on his face. He stopped in the center of the room, the frown on his face deepened. "Our victory depends on a surprise attack. Take every precaution, gentlemen."

A sergeant appeared suddenly and stood saluting.

"What are you doing here?" demanded Washington in quick anger.

"Making beds, sir," said the sergeant. "Do you wish for water, sir?"

"We wish for nothing." Washington made a gesture for him to go out through the entry.

The sergeant saluted and hurried out past the sentries without looking at them.

"Walls have ears," said Hamilton, mysteriously. "They say there is a spy, but no one is certain."

"Keep an eye on the man," Washington frowned darkly.

The sergeant was in the kitchen whispering with the cook when Hamilton found him at last.

"There's to be punch for the officers on Christmas Eve," grinned the sergeant with an innocent air.

Hamilton was not at all convinced that the sergeant and the cook were talking about punch. And yet they might have been, mused Hamilton. There was a large punch bowl standing on the table. Where did the cook get it, and what had they to make punch with, he wondered as he went to report his suspicions to Washington.

Christmas Eve came around in a storm of snow and sleet. The men in the encampment were not celebrating Christmas Eve. A rumor was being circulated in deep secret. They were to attack the Hessians at Trenton. At supper, an officer had announced that deserters would be caught and flogged without quarter. Bill and Nat, not on duty this evening, relaxed in the light of the wood fire.

"At home now," Bill said half aloud, "they're singing carols maybe. There's a tree with presents and there's fruitcake and there's a yule log in the fireplace, and wreaths in the windows and mistle-toe —" Bill fell silent, thinking of his folks at home and of Nellie, his sweetheart, smiling from behind the window curtains, waiting for him to come home.

He looked around the dreary barracks, half dug-out, half built of roughhewn logs. He had had enough of this war, he thought to himself. Flogging or no flogging, he was going to get away from here before the night was over. His mind was made up. He had it all planned.

The men were whispering, telling each other what they had heard, trying to figure it out.

"Something's up all right. General Washington's been talking to the officers in secret —"

"Ay, and the sergeants are taking inventory of ammunition, and have ordered us to have guns and bayonets cleaned and ready."

"Maybe it's just to keep us occupied," speculated Nat.

Bill listened to the talk, but it didn't matter to him, he told himself. He was clearing out this very night. He unwrapped the rags around his feet and tried to warm his frostbitten toes with the palms of his hands. A pair of officer's boots he had found in the rubbish heap were tucked away under the straw sack that served for a bed. The boots had no soles, but they would keep his rags from slipping off his feet when he walked through the deep snow.

He knew of a Quaker a few miles away. The Quaker, reasoned Bill, did not believe in war. If he could manage to get to that Quaker's farm, he would be safe. The Quaker would certainly let him remain hidden in the hay if he found him in his barn on Christmas Day. Bill felt in his pocket. He had managed to hide one of the wretched potatoes to take with him. It would keep him from starving in case he had to stay in hiding longer than he hoped.

An officer entered the dugout suddenly. He had a solemn expression on his weatherbeaten face. He did not say "Merry Christmas," but he said in a calm clear voice, "This is Christmas Eve, my men." He sat down on a pile of firewood, and looked around him at the uneasy faces, and said, after a moment's silence, "You all know Thomas Paine, aide-de-camp to General Greene — a good man. Didn't mind what he turned his hand to, nursed and cooked on occasion." The officer talked in a friendly voice.

"Ay, we know Tom Paine," called out several voices.

"Tom Paine wrote a pamphlet; he called it *The Crisis* because we're in a crisis," went on the officer. "It's full of gunpowder; it's like a cannon fired inside of you." The officer looked around at the inquiring puzzled faces staring at him. "Well, we need it," he said quietly. He opened the pamphlet he was holding in his hand, and began to read aloud:

" 'These are the times that try men's souls. The summer soldier and the sunshine patriot will, in this crisis, shrink from the service of their country. But he that stands it *now*, deserves the love and thanks of men and women.' " The officer glanced up for a moment and went on reading. " 'Tyranny, like hell, is not easily conquered; yet we have this consolation with us, that the harder the conflict, the more glorious the triumph.' " The officer's voice rang out in the twilight with challenge. " '. . . Freedom should . . . be highly rated. . . . I call not upon a few, but upon all . . .' "

Bill sat with his shoulders hunched, his face turned away. He tried not to listen to the reading, but it seemed to him that every word rang out in the stillness like thunder.

The officer cleared his throat and went on reading, " '. . . I love the man that can smile in trouble, that can gather strength from distress, and grow brave by reflection.' "

"That's the way Washington is," Nat nudged Bill. Bill moved uneasily. His face felt hot. There was sweat on his forehead, but his spine felt cold. It seemed to him that every word the officer read was addressed to him. If only he would stop reading that thing! But the officer kept it up. " '. . . I thank God that I fear not. I see no real cause for fear. I know our situation well, and can see the way out of it.' " The reading stopped suddenly. The officer looked around cautiously at the men.

"Read more," called out several voices. Bill shifted from side to side. All he wanted was to get away.

" '. . . We are fighting to make a new world, not for ourselves only but for all those yet unborn. . . .' " The officer read on and stopped.

"Tom Paine marched with us from Germantown," whispered one of the men, nudging his companion.

"Ay," grunted the other, "we were beaten, and Tom Paine says to us — 'Men live by glory,' he says — 'Our cause is just,' he says."

The officer listened to them in silence for a while. "Yes, Tom Paine said many things we need to think about now — good night, men, rest well." The officer left them as abruptly as he had come.

"I saw Tom Paine write that pamphlet." Nat edged closer to Bill. "He wrote it on top of a drum he held between his knees. He was a man to stir you to the heart," ruminated Nat. "He made you understand." Bill remained motionless, his head on his knees. He did not want to look at Nat.

Nat fell silent at last, thinking of General Washington — the General looked tired these days; he hardly took time to rest, pacing the floor, thinking, thinking, thinking. If it were true that he had decided to attack Trenton, he must have a good reason.

"Washington is a brave general, he is also a wise general. I am with him in everything he decides to do." Nat turned to Bill again. "Washington is not thinking of his own safety. He is thinking only of the revolution, and that is all that counts." But Bill, sitting there with his head on his knees, did not seem to hear him.

Some of them would not come back, thought Nat. Perhaps it would be he. Nat's thoughts switched to his wife and his small son, waiting for him at home. He remembered the day he left for the army; and now suddenly he understood more clearly that grand and proud feeling he had that day, and what Washington meant when he made his brief remarks, and what Jefferson meant when he wrote the Declaration of Independence. They were fighting for something larger than all of them put together. They were fighting for Liberty. They would win. Washington didn't doubt, neither would he. Yes, they would win, they must. He went to sleep thinking of that.

Bill lay awake listening to the men talking. They were sure now that there was to be an attack on Trenton. They talked and speculated and went off to sleep at last. Bill felt his heart pounding against his ribs. It seemed to him that everyone must hear it, it sounded so loud. He leaned on his elbow thinking and planning. In the corner of the hut, there was a hole under the rubble, large enough for a man to crawl out, if he lay flat on his stomach.

Bill stared at the dying embers in the ashes. He tried not to think of anything but the way to get to that hole without waking anyone. But instead, thoughts about George Washington swarmed in his head. In the darkness, he saw his face as if he were there: pale and very tired. Bill tried to push this image out of his mind. But he couldn't; and he remembered, now, the kind look in his eyes when he looked at them and cheered them when everything seemed lost.

"Don't think of yesterday; think of tomorrow" — that was the way he talked. He never gave up. "Men live by glory" — who said that, wondered Bill, and remembered it was Tom Paine said it. He had heard Tom Paine say it. What the officer had been reading to them came back to him now with a terrible impact. If he ran away, he would be a deserter. A shameful feeling came to Bill — and suddenly he knew that he could not be a deserter. No matter what happened, he would remain and face it. He would take part and do his share. He lay back on his bunk and closed his eyes. He was not frightened any more, not hating war. A wonderful relief and gladness came to him now. He curled up, pulled the tattered covers around him, and went to sleep.

At Trenton, the Tories were celebrating Christmas on a grand scale. The war was practically over, they told each other. By spring, the rebel army will run home to their plowing, their stores and offices, and whatever they had been doing before they took it into their foolish heads that they wanted Liberty.

Colonel Rahl and his twelve hundred Hessians received many invitations to dinners and to parties. At the large house where the Colonel was encamped with his staff of officers and orderlies there were many guests on Christmas Day. There was singing and dancing, and a great dinner with much wine. They drank toasts to victory and told jokes about the American Army.

"The American Army, where is it?" Lieutenant

Piel laughed. "The war is all over. Easter we go home to Germany." The lady he was dancing with understood only a few words of German. She laughed because she thought he was telling a funny story. "It is true," the Lieutenant said earnestly. "What is left of the American Army is hiding in holes." He let out a loud laugh, and the lady laughed with him because now she felt certain he was telling a funny story.

Colonel Rahl tried to dance too, but he did not feel very steady on his feet after drinking so many toasts to victory. He stepped on his partner's toes, and begged to be excused. He spoke only a few words in English and the lady spoke only a few words in German. A buzz of many voices filled the house; everybody was talking and singing German songs. The Colonel liked the songs. He clapped his hands and invited the ladies to sing with him.

"It will be spring soon; we will go home," cried a lieutenant.

"Yes, spring is beautiful in Germany," Major Von Dechow joined the conversation.

"Flowers, roses, oh roses," muttered Colonel Rahl.

It was hot in the room, though the windows rattled with the wind and the patter of sleet on the panes. Captain Altenbochen was the only one not too drunk to feel uneasy. He had something on his mind; he wanted to think it out. The room was full of tobacco smoke and there was too much noise, with everybody singing, talking, and laughing so loud. But some of the guests were going home at last. He was glad; he went out to get a breath of air.

A sharp wind and a shower of sleet beat against his face. He walked down the path a little way and peered into the inky darkness. If the Americans, he thought to himself, if they found out there was no patrol — what then, eh, he asked himself in the darkness. What if a spy reported to the Americans that their camp was unfortified? Colonel Rahl had called in the patrol to celebrate Christmas; a risky thing, thought the Captain, wagging his head sadly. He looked around him uneasily and walked around to the back of the house. A man appeared from out of the darkness, all wrapped up in a greatcoat and many scarves.

"Who goes?" challenged the Captain in German.

The man stood still and saluted. "I must see the Colonel," he said in English.

"Credentials," barked the Captain, peering into the man's face. Recognizing one of the Tories, he heaved a sigh of relief. The man fished in his pocket and handed the Captain a crumpled piece of paper.

Another invitation, thought the Captain. "*Danke schön*," he said in German, dismissing the man with a wave of the hand. The man bowed and trudged away in the darkness.

Captain Altenbochen returned to the house and leaned over the Colonel, now playing chess with Lieutenant Kiemm who did not know how to play chess and tried to bluff. But the Colonel didn't mind; he couldn't quite remember whose move it was.

"If the Americans find out we have no patrol tonight? If they attack? The camp is unfortified," Captain Altenbochen blurted out.

"*Donner und Blitzen*," roared the Colonel. "The Americans are fools, but they aren't such fools. Not even a dog would go out on a night like this."

"Maybe, maybe," mumbled the Captain foolishly, and handed the Colonel the note.

The Colonel unfolded the scrap of paper, and tried to read what was written there. If only those Tories could realize that he didn't know how to read English, he muttered, annoyed. He looked around him now for someone to translate the note to him. His American and English guests had gone home. Well, it didn't matter, just another invitation, no doubt, or a request for a favor; he knew those Tories. They were never satisfied! He sighed. He felt very sleepy. He tucked the note into his pocket and climbed the stairs to his room. The bed was neat and waiting. He tumbled into it half undressed, the note safe in his pocket. On it was written in English, "The Americans are going to attack to-night."

At this very moment, Washington and his men were marching down to the Delaware River. The wind, loaded with sleet, whipped their faces and blinded them. Their feet left bloody footmarks in the snow. But no one seemed to be aware of the cold and snow. Only one thought occupied them now: "This time, they must win a victory." At the ferry crossing, Washington discovered that neither Putnam, Ewing, nor Caldwater had come. The storm was evidently too much for them. Washington looked at his men, taking their measure in one swift glance. He must make the attack alone with these twenty-four hundred men, and Glover's Marblehead fishermen to man the boats.

There was pity and pride in Washington's eyes as he watched the Marblehead boys take charge. They were used to storms at sea and to ice. Not one of them flinched. They faced the wind and sleet, expert and steadfast. Bill paused for one brief instant as he marched past Washington to take his place. Their eyes met, and in the hushed stillness, it seemed to Bill as if Washington spoke and said, "It is better to die for a great cause than to live for little things."

He would remember this moment all his life, Bill thought to himself as the boats, tossed by wind and contrary current, plowed their way through sheets of floating ice.

The crossing took longer than Washington expected. It was four o'clock in the morning by the time the last boat touched the Trenton shore. And now there were six miles to march to the village street where the Hessians were encamped. They walked in silence, knee-deep in the snow. It was slow marching. All was still, not a dog was in sight to bark a warning to the sleeping village. Every house, covered by a coat of snow, was shrouded in darkness. Washington separated his men into two divisions: one under Greene marched up inland; Sullivan marched his division along the riverbank.

Bill marched beside Nat; he wanted to talk to him. Nat looked very calm and sure of himself. Bill swallowed hard; there was a strange feeling inside of him and he wanted to shout and to sing. He craned his neck to look toward Washington. How straight and tall he was, and his face stern as if he were made of stone. But there was a glint of fire in those gray eyes now. Bill felt very humble. He had a great desire to do something to prove that he was with him, not only in body but in spirit also. And at this moment each word Tom Paine wrote in the pamphlet the officer had read to them the night before took on a new meaning.

A messenger from Sullivan ran up to Washington now. "The muskets are wet, sir. They can't be fired," he said in a hoarse whisper.

"Tell your general to use the bayonets; the town must be taken," snapped Washington in a commanding voice.

A gray line of light appeared on the horizon. The black night was coming to an end. They had not much farther to go now. The long village street stretched before them wide and straight. Sullivan's men charged up the road with their bayonets, shouting at the top of their lungs.

The houses came alive, doors and windows flew open, shouts and screams rang out in the gray dawn. Hessians, only half dressed, were pouring out into the streets; bullets and bayonets greeted them from all sides. The bewildered Hessians, roused so suddenly from their drunken slumbers, swarmed and churned in circles, and tried to escape by the Brunswick Road. Sullivan's bayonets barred the way, and Washington sent riflemen to cut off escape.

Bill fought like mad. He felt a little sick at the sight of so many Hessians lying in pools of blood in the snow. He saw Colonel Rahl rush out of the house shouting orders to his men. The Colonel was hardly dressed, his jacket gaped open, his chest was bare. He was entirely sober now as he rushed back and forth trying to pull his men together to make a stand. Hessian soldiers brought out arms hastily. But Americans met them with bullets flying in all directions, from every side. Bayonets glimmered in the half-light, rifle shots rang out and pelted them like rain. Americans were shouting and singing. Bill kept on firing . . . He saw Rahl hit by a bullet. He saw him fall in the snow and lie still, blood running from his wound. A moment of terrible pity came to him. But it was all over now, he realized; the Hessians were laying down their arms.

"They are surrendering," shouted Nat.

Shouts of victory rang from every side.

Washington was saying something in a quiet voice. Bill could not make out what he said; but he could see Washington's face, no longer tired, nor stern, but strangely calm.

The Hessians stood unarmed now, their faces sullen.

"We must have got nearly a thousand Hessians," said Nat with pride, "and all their weapons and loot. Some of 'em escaped, about thirty killed, and some wounded." Nat felt shaky too. He wanted to talk to relieve his feelings . . . "Our revolution is safe now," he continued. "Those who thought we were finished will take heart and come to our aid. That's what this battle means, Bill."

Washington, in a voice charged with compassion, was giving orders to care for the wounded. Bill began to help Nat carry groaning men into nearby houses. There will be more battles, Bill was thinking. But we'll win because our cause is just.

Nat was talking to him again in a low voice as if he wanted to make him share something he was seeing. "This is not for ourselves only —" Nat was thinking of his small son at home — "it is for our children and for all those not yet born."

Washington turned to talk to General Greene now, making swift plans: "The Hessians shall parade through the streets in Philadelphia. Let the Tories see the revolution is not over. We'll send the Hessian flag to Baltimore to hang in the Hall of Congress. Men of goodwill will take heart."

"Men of goodwill will take heart," General Greene repeated thankfully. "They will come to our aid."

Washington looked around at his men in wordless gratitude. This victory was their victory. He wanted them to know it.

The Old Soldier

by Dorothy Canfield

No matter how I set this story down, you will take it, I fear, as a fable. But it is not. It is as literally true as a local news item in your this-morning's newspaper. It happened up the state aways from our town, "over the mountain," as we call that middle upland valley of Vermont.

For a long time, after the Revolution, the little town of Sunmore had made a great day out of the Fourth of July. They seemed to hear, more clearly than some other towns, the very sound of the old Liberty Bell in Philadelphia as it rang out in joy over the signing of the Declaration of Independence. They had not at all forgotten what the Fourth meant. As the years went by, a set form grew up for the day's celebration. At dawn, the big boys fired off again and again the old cannon which stood on the village common. There was a meeting, about eleven in the morning, at the Town Hall, where people made speeches, and sang patriotic songs. After that, a picnic lunch was eaten out on the green. If it rained, the lunch was eaten inside the Town Hall. Then, rain or shine, the procession formed to escort the old soldiers out to the Burying Ground, a mile from town, where they put flags on the graves of their comrades among the Sunmore men, who, like them, had been soldiers in the Revolution.

Nearly everybody in town marched in this procession, carrying flags and flowers and keeping step with the music of the town drum and fife corps. "Whee-dee-deedle-dee" went the high thin voices of the fifes; and "boom-boom-boom" went the deep voices of the drums. Tramp! tramp! tramp! went the feet of the Sunmore men and women and children — especially boys.

The boys looked forward to this celebrating from one year to the next, chiefly of course because to share in the firing of the cannon marked a long step forward in growing up. The cannon was generally said to have been in the Battle of Bennington in 1777. Ordinary people said yes of course it was. But more careful folks said this was not sure. As the years went by after that battle, twenty, forty, fifty, and finally by the time of this story, in 1848, seventy years, fewer and fewer people could remember it. And of course there were fewer and fewer old Sunmore men who had been Revolutionary soldiers.

Until they were past eighty, they had walked in the procession like everybody else. After that, Dr. White, who of course took care of them all when they were sick, said their joints were too stiff. He took them out in his own chaise, behind his slow, ancient roan horse. Dick was rather stiff in his joints too, and was glad to walk with ceremonial slowness.

Dr. White knew more about medicine than anyone else in town. This was to be expected because nobody else knew anything at all about it. But on the subject — local history — of which many people knew a great deal, he was also the local specialist. On the shelves of his library, mixed up with his medical books, stood more histories of Vermont than the rest of Sunmore people had, all put together. When anyone wanted to find out something about what had happened in the past, Dr. White was asked. He always knew the answer.

When May and June came in, people began to plan for the Fourth of July celebration. But there were no old soldiers left. For four or five years there had been only two. Both of them were very old of course, for the year 1848 was seventy-one years after the Battle of Bennington. One had been ninety, and the other eighty-six. Now both were gone. The older one had died in the winter, and the family of the other one had moved away out west into York State and taken the old man with them.

It was too bad. Everybody was saying that the celebration wouldn't be much without old soldiers in it, to connect the town with the Revolution. Without one, how would people remember what the Fourth of July was really about? The ancients had always sat on the platform of the Town Hall, while the singing and speech-making went on, their long firearms across their knees, their soldier's leather belts strapped on over their Sunday coats. Of course what uniforms they had had, had gone all to pieces, if they'd ever had any, which was unlikely, buckskin being the wear in those early days. They had ridden in Dr. White's chaise, just behind the fife and drum corps, and the little girls in white dresses carrying the bouquets, ahead of the marching men and women, four abreast in the road. When the procession reached the cemetery, the little girls handed the flowers to the big boys, and they passed them out to the hobbling old soldiers, who laid them on the graves of their comrades in the Revolution. The smaller boys had the honor of planting fresh American flags on the graves, waving above the flowers.

One of the boys in town, one of the Bostwick family, heard his folks lamenting that the celebration would not seem right with no old soldiers at all. He was the third child, Andrew was his name; he was about ten years old when this happened. He went to the nearby district school and read in the fourth reader, but long before he knew his alphabet, he knew about the Battle of Bennington and the Revolutionary War.

He was just getting to be old enough to help fire off the cannon, and to hand the flowers to the old soldiers in the cemetery. And now they were all gone.

One day in June, when he was sent out to look for a cow which, the night before, hadn't come back to the barn from the mountain pasture, he met a schoolmate up there, Will Hunter. Will's mother had sent him out to pick wild strawberries on that sloping clearing. After the two boys met, the cow and the strawberries were forgotten. They sat down on a ledge to have a talk. Before long Andrew said something about the Fourth of July celebration with no old soldier left, not a single one.

The other boy said, "There's an old fellow lives with the Hawleys, 'way up Hawley Hollow from our house. He's their great-grandfather, I think. Maybe he was a soldier in the Revolution. He's old enough. They say he's ninety. More."

Andrew's ten-year-old mind was already firmly lodged behind the tight narrow wall of the idea of the Town. "They don't live in Sunmore," he said. "We have to have a Sunmore old soldier for our Fourth."

"Yes, they do too, live in Sunmore," said the other boy. "They don't trade at the Sunmore stores much, because from that end of the Hollow where their house is, it's easier to go out the far end to Canbury. But they vote in our Town Meeting."

The two boys looked at each other. Thinking no more of the cow and the strawberries they set out for Hawley Hollow.

So there *was* to be a Revolutionary soldier after all for the Fourth of July celebration! Everybody was talking about the old man, eighty-nine years, or maybe ninety, maybe more, back up on the far side of Westward Mountain, who had been remembered just in time. When the two boys told their fathers about him, two of the Selectmen of the town had gone over the mountain to see him. They said his back was bent with rheumatism, he was almost stone deaf, and he hobbled along with two canes to steady him. But he still had his old rifle, and even his cracked leather soldier's belt, just as the others had. And they reported that when, shouting loudly in his ear, they had asked him if he had fought in the Revolutionary War, he had nodded his head. Then they asked had it been in the Battle of Bennington? When he finally heard what they were asking he nodded his head and told them, "Yes, yes, *sir*, it certainly was."

They said the Hawleys up there, for all he was so old, thought a great deal of him. It was his great-grandson's family he was with — young people they were, had been married only five or six years. When the last of his grandchildren had died of old age, these young people had left their little cottage in Canbury and gone up to take care of him. An arrangement often made, in our country — he was to leave them his house and farm and they were to provide for his old age. They had never heard, naturally, what he had been doing seventy years ago — neither of them was over twenty-five — but they had always seen the old long gun, laid on the pegs over the fireplace, and the old belt hung with it.

Wasn't it remarkable, Sunmore people said, that just that very year when the last of the old heroes had gone, this other old Revolutionary soldier had been found. And who had found him? Why Andrew

Bostwick and William Hunter, two little boys. They were bright little boys to have known enough history to understand about the Fourth of July. Patriotic too. The program committee arranged that they were to stand on the platform during the meeting on each side of the old soldier, and to march in the procession just in front of Dr. White's chaise, each one carrying an American flag. They were to be called the "Young Guard of Honor." You don't need anyone to tell you that those boys could hardly wait for the Fourth of July to come.

On the morning of the Fourth, Andrew's father got up early, took the boys, and drove his farm wagon all the way around the mountain and up into the Hollow to bring the old man back. It was ten o'clock when they came back into Sunmore Street. A crowd was waiting in front of the Town Hall. They began to clap their hands and cheer when Mr. Boswick helped lift the bent old man out of the wagon and led him into the Hall. Andrew and Will, the Young Guard of Honor, carried his ancient gun in and put it across his knees. He had his rusty belt strapped on over his coat.

When they took his gun to carry, he gave them such a pleasant smile of thanks that they understood why his great-grandchildren thought so much of him. He was a very nice-looking old man, everybody thought, clean and neat, with quiet gentle eyes; and although he hadn't a tooth left, his mouth still looked as though he liked jokes.

The people came into the Town Hall, took their seats, and began fanning themselves. It was a hot day, as the Fourth often is. The speaker was there, a lawyer from Canbury. The chorus of local singers stood below the platform, facing the audience. Their leader rapped his stick. They stood at attention. But they did not begin to sing. For at this point Dr. White, who always sat on the platform with the Selectmen and the speaker, called out to Andrew, "Here! Let me look at that gun! Pass it over to me."

Andrew was surprised. He put his hand on the gun, and leaning down to the old man's ear said to him as loudly as he could, "Dr. White wants to see your gun."

He shouted with all his might but he could not make himself heard. The old soldier was almost stone deaf. But he was willing to do anything that was wanted. His cheerful old face was bright. He felt the friendliness all around him. He smiled and nodded and passed his gun to Andrew.

The doctor took one sharp look at it and motioned to the singers in the chorus. "Wait a minute!" he told them.

Then he put on his glasses (he was the first

person in Sunmore to have spectacles) , and looked very carefully at a certain place near the trigger. Everybody kept still, wondering what was in his mind.

When he looked up, his face was all astonishment. He spoke so loudly that everybody in the whole Town Hall could hear him. "This is a Hessian gun! The old man must have been one of the Hessians who fought against the Americans."

There was such a silence in the Town Hall you could hear a wasp buzzing at one of the windows.

He was a Hessian! He had fought on the other side. People's mouths dropped open, they were so taken back.

The old man hadn't heard any of this because he was so deaf. He sat quietly there, between the two little boys, his gentle old eyes looking around at the people in the hall.

For a minute nobody said a word. Nobody could think what to say. Or what to do.

Then Andrew ran out to the front of the platform and began to talk very fast. "Listen," he said. "That was a hundred years ago. Well, more than seventy years anyhow. No matter how mad you are at somebody, you don't keep it up forever. The Bible says not to. He's lived close to us all that time, and farmed it like anybody, and had his family, and paid his taxes. He's old, so old — it would be *mean* of us to —"

Andrew had never even spoken a piece in school. He had forgotten where he was. When he realized what he was doing, he stopped talking and hung down his head. He went back and put one hand on the old man's shoulder. The wrinkled face lifted to smile at him. Andrew smiled back. But his lips were trembling.

People began to rustle and move their feet. But when Dr. White stood up as if to say something, they were still again, to listen.

He said, "I remember now, when I came to Sunmore to practice medicine and first began to be interested in Vermont history, I did hear some very old people talk about a young Hessian soldier who had been wounded in the Battle of Bennington, and was picked up unconscious, in the woods, the day after. One of the old history books in my Vermont collection says that he was carried to a farmhouse and taken care of there. By the time he was well enough to get around, many months afterwards, there were no more soldiers or armies around. He was only nineteen by that time, and he had come to love the way of life he saw around him. He wanted to be an American and live here.

"That history book didn't say anything more about him. But I heard something else from old Mr. Hale." The doctor looked down into the audience at a middle-aged man in the second row. "He was your grandfather, Jim Hale. He was sort of connected, in-laws somehow, with the Bennington family that took in the Hessian boy. He told me they always liked him, the young soldier, I mean. When he learned enough English, he told them his story. He had always had it hard in the Old Country, he said. He was an orphan, very poor, seventeen years old, when a recruiting gang picked him up off the street and carried him off to the barracks in Brunswick. He never liked soldiering, he said. He never understood what the fighting was about, because he never knew any English till he learned it from the Vermont family who took care of him."

The doctor still held the old rifle in his hands. He turned around now and laid it back on the old man's knees. Then he said to the audience, "I rather think Andrew Bostwick was right. Seventy years is too long to go on being mad. I think our celebration would better go on. Maybe the Reverend Hardwick might have something to say to us about this."

The minister stood up, stooped in his black clergyman's clothes.

The old man from Hawley Hollow had evidently thought the program was going on, and that the doctor had been making one of the planned-for speeches. Now, seeing the minister stand up and step forward, he thought that the prayer was to be said. He composed his face, leaned forward in his chair in the respectful position you take when somebody is praying in public, and dropped his eyes to the ground.

As a matter of fact, the Reverend Hardwick did pray. He stood silent a long time. Then he said, "May war pass and peace be with us. Amen."

He sat down. The Moderator of the Town stood up. He was a burly, powerful, middle-aged man, with a serious, responsible face. He said, soberly, "I think this is something we ought to take a vote on. Don't you think so, Mr. Hardwick?"

The minister nodded. "Yes. It is something for each one of us to decide. But before we vote, I think we ought to sit quiet for a moment. And think."

The Moderator reached for the clergyman's cane, and with it struck a gavel-like blow on the table. In his Moderator's voice, he said, "The question before this House, is whether we can live in peace when war has long gone by."

They all sat still.

The deaf ears of the old soldier had, of course, not heard any of this. It looked all right to him. He was very much bent with rheumatism. His hands lay thin and knotted on the arms of his chair. His clean old face was calm. In the silence he looked from one person to another in the audience. He smiled a little. After a moment, he turned his white head to look back at his little-boy guard of honor. There they were, one on each side of his chair. He nodded, and leaned back as if to say, "It's all right, if you are there."

The water came into Andrew's eyes.

The people in the rows of chairs on the floor were all looking up at the old soldier and the little boys.

A man stood up and said, "Mr. Moderator, I move that our celebration proceed."

Several voices said, "I second the motion."

Then the vote was taken. Everybody voted "aye."

So that afternoon, after the usual speaking and singing had been done, and the picnic lunch eaten out on the Common, the procession formed as usual, to march out to the cemetery.

The old soldier looked very tired by this time, but still cheerful. He came out of the Town Hall on Dr. White's arm, and was helped up into the chaise. The Young Guard of Honor held their flags high, so that they stirred in the breeze. The little girls in white dresses were pushed by their mothers into line, two by two. They carried the flowers, lilies, roses, carnation pinks.

The men and women formed, four by four. The doctor slapped the reins over the old horse's back. The leader of the band lifted his hand and said, commandingly, "A-a-all ready!"

The marchers held their flags straight.

"Forward, *march!*" cried the bandmaster.

The fifes sang out "Whee-dee-deedle-dee" in thin high voices.

In a deep roar, the drums said, "Boom! boom! boom!"

And away they all went.

IN THE
WAR OF 1812
1812-1815

From

Commander-in-Chief James Madison

From our country's earliest days, freedom on the sea has been cherished equally with freedom on land. When, therefore, our ships were boarded and searched by the British, President James Madison on June 1, 1812, reluctantly asked Congress for a Declaration of War:

"We behold, in fine, a state of war against the United States and on the side of the United States a state of peace against Great Britain. . . . Whether the United States shall continue passive under these progressive usurpations and these accumulating wrongs or, opposing force to force in defense of their national rights . . . is a solemn question which the Constitution wisely confides to the legislative department of the Government."

From

Commander Andrew Jackson

By the time he was fourteen years of age, Andrew Jackson knew what war meant for he had lost his father and mother and two brothers in the American Revolution, and had himself engaged in skirmishes against the British. As a young man, he joined the State Militia of Tennessee, becoming a major general in 1802. In the War of 1812, he was made a commander, leading his troops to victory against the British in the Battle of New Orleans on January 8, 1815. In a letter written to a friend at that time, he said:

"Our Union, it must be preserved."

Battle of New Orleans

by Meredith Nicholson

"You'll eat your Christmas Dinner in New Orleans!" Cochrane, the British Admiral, had boasted
to the men of his fleet.

On the twenty-third of December it seemed possible that he would keep his promise. The British
controlled Lake Borgne, but between it and New Orleans lay a diversity of bayous, cypress swamps, dikes
and ditches not pleasing to a lord admiral of the
sea. Sailors and redcoats poled their way in barges
through Bayou Bienview and camped on Villere's
plantation. Young Major Villere, escaping under
a fusillade of British musket-balls, galloped into the
city and gave warning of the enemy's approach.

At the Royal Street house Andrew Jackson received the news calmly; issued orders swiftly. Commodore Patterson with the schooners *Carolina* and
Louisiana was ordered down the river: John Coffee
was in motion with his mounted riflemen who,

cheerful souls, had brought along their hunting knives and hatchets. Batteries of artillery rumbled to the front. The Orleans Rifle Company, the Mississippi Dragoons, companies of regulars, battalions of the free Negroes which Jackson had urged into the service, and a band of Choctaws in war paint were flung forward to arrest the invader.

Contemptuous reports of the American forces were borne back to the British commanders by the withdrawing pickets. It was near the end of the day and no offensive was expected from the oddly assorted battalions of Americans visible on the New Orleans road.

Andrew Jackson, worn with his day's labors, flung himself on a couch and slept half an hour while Fowler replaced the orderly at the door and received reports. Waking refreshed, the commander ate a few spoonfuls of rice as he listened to Fowler's recital of the disposition of the troops.

"The enemy are camped on Villere's plantation. They'll hardly strike until they have reinforcements from their fleet."

"Patterson's on the way down the river? Good. Is Livingston here?"

"Yes; and he reports the Louisiana militia in fine spirits and anxious to show their patriotism. Your orders are all executed. Governor Claiborne remains

in town with General Carroll's troops to guard
against a flank movement."

"Get the staff together and we'll ride down to the
front. If things look right we'll stir 'em up a little
tonight," commanded Jackson.

The shadows of the winter twilight gathered
upon the plain. Jackson gazed across the British
bivouac, brilliantly lighted by their campfires. He
sent a messenger to signal Patterson on the *Carolina*
to begin firing when he got in position.

The British, not expecting an attack, thought the
American schooner a trading ship and were aware
of their error only when the cannon began booming.
The campfires were at once extinguished, but the
sudden assault, followed at once by vigorous pressure by the American line, shook the morale of the
invaders and they were slow in forming to resist
the attack. For two hours and a half the battle raged
in the dark. Bayonets on the British side and hunting knives in the hands of the Kentuckians and
Tennesseans were plied fiercely as the battle lines
clashed and clinched. This hand-to-hand fighting
in the dark, against a foe of uncertain numbers,
with black and red faces to contend with and wild
white men in caps made of the skins of wild beasts,
was not like warfare in Europe! To add to the din
and confusion the little *Carolina* belched hot shot

at intervals and now and again the terrified red-coats heard the shrill high voice of the American commander shouting orders, cheering on his men.

A smothering fog drifted up from the sea and Jackson decided to risk no more that night. Not so formidable, those British! He would wait for a chance to clean them up in daylight.

"This is only a little Christmas fandango," he remarked to Coffee. "They've got to hurry if they hand Louisiana to their king for a Christmas present!"

"We've picked up seventy-four prisoners," Reid reported. "They thought they'd march right into town but this night attack's chilled 'em. There'll hardly be another move till the big chief arrives — General Sir Edward Pakenham. His men say he'll make short work of us — he's brother-in-law to the Duke of Wellington."

"Let 'em send the duke!" said Jackson with a sardonic grin. "We'll take him home to Nashville in a basket!"

In the gray dawn of Christmas morning the American pickets reported that the night had been marked by great activity in the British camp. The enemy had pushed forward their artillery and additional infantry. Within a few hours lusty cheering announced that Pakenham had arrived to take command.

Coffee feinted at intervals with detachments of cavalry and the *Carolina,* hanging along the west bank of the river, dropped a shot into the enemy's camp occasionally.

"Keep 'em worried," were Jackson's orders. "We need time to establish our lines."

The city and the neighboring plantations were ransacked for picks and spades and with furious energy the Americans began building entrenchments. Not for nothing had the commander established military law! All the horses, oxen and mules in the region were hauling timbers and cotton bales to strengthen the breastworks. Soft-handed citizens accepted without grumbling the rough labor assigned them. Mutinous mutterings were silenced as Jackson rode the lines, scolding, praising, exacting every ounce of strength the hard-driven laborers could bring to their task. He had established headquarters in a planter's house close to the breastworks, and partaking sparingly of his rice ration and sleeping not at all, he strengthened and lengthened his line.

The insolence of the *Carolina* having at last become insufferable, Pakenham planted his heaviest ordnance on the levee and for half an hour the little vessel gallantly responded to the British cannon. Set on fire by a hot ball that landed near her powder chests the commander gave orders to abandon ship. The crew fired a final broadside and left her only a few minutes before she blew up with a mighty explosion.

The *Louisiana* got away to the western side of the river and Jackson turned his spy-glass upon the enemy's land forces.

Posted on the levee, the sick man from the Hermitage summarized recent history with satisfaction. Pakenham might be a great strategist by European standards, but he had dallied three days in the presence of an enemy greatly inferior on land and sea when he might have eaten his Christmas pudding in New Orleans if he had made a determined offensive.

"By the Eternal! He'll never get there!" Jackson declared, and turned to find Jean Lafitte beside him. A modest gentleman, the pirate of Barataria! He merely wished to announce that his men, among them skilled artillerists, had been assigned to service in keeping with their talents and that they would give a good account of themselves.

"My frien's of Barataria know not the word fear! They know onl-ee to fight and die!" he declared. "In what way can I serve you, Generale Jacksone?"

Jackson, pleased with his zeal, gave him a message to carry with all speed to Commodore Patterson across the river. The British were already advancing in two magnificent columns as if on parade. One line moved along the river, the other skirted the fringes of a cypress swamp. Ignorant of the extent of the American entrenchments, the British veterans marched to within six hundred yards of the American lines only to falter and retreat before a devastating fire.

Pakenham, knighted for valor at Salamanca over yonder in Spain, watched with amazement and mortification the repulse of the best troops in the British Army by American backwoodsmen. Through his glass he had caught a glimpse the day before of the American commander, who wasn't a general at all — only a frontier farmer and a sick man at that! Pestiferous fellows, those Tennessee riflemen; every time one fired there was a redcoat the less. A poor yarn this adventure would make for the drawing-rooms when he got back to London! To echoing cheers from the American lines he withdrew bewildered, to confer with Cochrane, the admiral.

Neither Sir Edward nor the admiral understood the ways of the Americans. They were constantly abroad on terrifying errands. Most annoying were the movements of Tom Hinds, a young and handsome Mississippian. Hinds, abroad on reconnaissance duty, swept with a company of dragoons close to British batteries, delivered a deadly musket fire and galloped away in safety. Even more fearsome were Coffee's Tennesseans, in their homespun, prowling about at night, a terror to pickets, stragglers and reconnoitering parties.

More guns must be brought from the ships and dragged through that thrice damned network of swamps and bayous! To add to the general joylessness, it rained frequently. The British seamen were vastly annoyed by the queer reptiles that snapped at their legs. At dusk the breeze wafted across the plain the mocking strains of a band attached to Planche's Orleans battalion playing the "Marseillaise"!

"Let all the bands play," Jackson ordered. "Music will be soothing to Sir Edward's feelings!"

He surveyed the wrecked British batteries grimly. He had won the day, but the greater struggle was yet to come. Ammunition was not reaching his lines as he expected, and he held Governor Claiborne responsible.

"Send me powder and ball or, by the Eternal, I'll cut off your head and ram it into a cannon!"

This clearly was no way to address a governor. Harassed by a thousand annoyances and tormented by pain, it was well that the commander's vituperative gifts afforded outlet for his emotions. Kentucky's long delayed phalanx arrived at New Orleans half clad and without arms. Jackson swore brilliantly, but ordered the city's shops and warehouses raided for equipment. He was giving personal attention to every detail of his defenses, guarding against every imaginable peril. He had established three successive lines of defense in case the first shouldn't hold. While the British were at their elaborate preparations the sick lord of the Hermitage had three thousand men strengthening his lines even though they had already survived massed infantry assaults and the thumping of cannon. The cotton bales used in the embrasures of some of the batteries failed to resist and Jackson replaced them with Delta mud, which, he had noted, sucked up cannon balls.

One o'clock in the morning. Fowler touched the commander's shoulder as he lay asleep in his uniform in the plantation house.

"What day is this?" Jackson demanded, at once on his feet buckling on his sword.

"The eighth of January. The enemy are preparing to attack. Butler has issued orders to all officers to be ready."

"Call Reid and come with me; we'll ride our lines. I want to see John Coffee."

He wanted to see John Coffee! It was comforting, indeed, on a murky morning, with a big job on hand, to have old Coffee within reach; fearless John Coffee, a military genius in his own right, but loved as a friend and neighbor. There was a moral stimulus to be got just from hearing the old fellow's gruff voice and feeling the touch of his hand. And Coffee, of course, was over there, where he had been told to be, at the edge of the cypress swamp with his men of the Cumberland. Many of them had slept on logs to lift them out of the slime.

As the day broke grudgingly a shotted rocket from the British lines hissed through the mists and fell into the river.

"The scoundrels have got to shoot better than that," Jackson commented to his staff as they watched the zigzag course of the fiery missile.

Pickets, falling back through the fog, announced the British advance. Out of the hovering mists they came, like an army with banners seen in a dream. A cannon boomed as an American gunner caught sight of them; then the fog curtained them again. The air was clearing and the Americans saw the approaching enemy — a magnificent pageant under the flags of their hard-won victories in the Old World.

Back of the center of his lines, unattended for the moment, Jackson saw them, knew that his great hour had come. In his breast pocket was his wife's last letter, and he thrust in his hand to touch it. He would not have Rachel ashamed of what he should do this day!

"Take your time, men," he was saying as he walked along his lines swinging his cane. "Be sure the squirrel's on your side of the tree before you shoot!"

The earth trembled as the American batteries thundered. Gaps in the solid British lines were quickly closed only to be ripped open again by murderous grape and canister. In mighty diapasons the cannon roared and in interludes the rifles of the frontiersmen caught up the strain with the rippling roll of a thousand drums. Good shots, those Baratarians! Jackson sent his compliments to Jean Lafitte. The British batteries, helpless to support the three thousand infantry that charged the American breastworks, fell back, confused, appalled by the pitiless hail of iron and lead that beat upon their faces. Gibbs, in immediate command of the movement, sought in vain to check the panic.

"Bring up the reserves!" Pakenham ordered,

urging his horse through his broken staggering army. His men regained confidence as General Keane flung in a regiment of Highlanders. Brave Scots! Two hundred perished in the raking fire of a single American cannon.

Pakenham in a frantic effort to rally his men rode to the head of his legion. Shot in the arm, he kept on. Falling a moment later, he died without knowing the extent of the catastrophe that had befallen his army.

Eight o'clock. The smoke cleared and the mounting sun revealed a trail of death on the miry plain. They lay in windrows — two thousand valiant Britons — as if cut down by some monstrous scythe. Only on the west bank of the river had the invaders won any advantage and this availed nothing as against the crushing defeat of the main army on the Chalmette plain.

Gazing across the blood-drenched field, Jackson raised his hand in salute.

"Brave fellows!" he exclaimed brokenly. "There are many of their wounded lying among the dead. Order the men to stop cheering and send our doctors over the field."

Quills were flying the next morning in the commander's headquarters; couriers groomed their horses for hard riding. Washington, Knoxville and Nashville must know the news. Sam Dale, a Mississippian, endeared to the commander by his feats of daring, was chosen to bear the news to the President. Coffee picked the other messengers from his Tennesseans — intrepid youngsters proud of the chance to carry the great news home to the neighbors. Jackson had Livingston, Reid and Fowler at work while he was still issuing orders to guard against a renewal of hostilities. Rachel must know from him the victory and he wrote her, first of all, to say that the British were whipped and that he himself was well.

I hope, my dear love, that you may join me here soon, but not until all is safe. The city is joyfully celebrating the triumph, but I remain on the field. My men have been bringing in a queer lot of odds and ends from the battlefield — the instruments of the Scotch Highlander's band, General Pakenham's chapeau, General Keane's trumpet and sword. The British threw away their guns as they ran and our men have been collecting them. You will gather from this the completeness of the rout. My best love to our dear boy. Be careful of yourself.

Amid all these moving scenes you fill my heart.
I am eager to be at the Hermitage again, but
while my country needs me we must sacrifice
our own happiness and peace.

He was busy with his report to President Madison
when his orderly handed him a paper. Incredible!
Only six Americans killed and seven wounded. The
British loss of more than two thousand included the
lieutenant general commanding, two major generals,
eight colonels, six majors, eighteen captains and
fifty-four lieutenants. On the west side of the river
the American casualties were one killed and five
wounded against the enemy's loss of one hundred
and twenty killed and wounded.

"God was with us!" exclaimed Jackson reverently.

"A committee of citizens to see you, General,"
reported Fowler.

"Thank them and say I'll not be ready for enter-
tainment till I've finished my business here. When
I go into the city I'll march with the men who won
the victory. We'll not do any bragging till we know
the enemy's satisfied. If they want more punishment
we must be ready to give it to 'em."

But with their most distinguished officers killed
and the rain-splashed plain one vast grave, the

British were already creeping back through the swamps to their ships, sending the conqueror a quite unnecessary request that he care for the wounded they were leaving behind.

IN THE WAR AGAINST MEXICO

1846-1848

From

Colonel Davy Crockett

This story of the Alamo is an authentic American historical document. For a long time it was thought that Davy Crockett was himself its sole author. Now it is believed to have been written after his death by friends who had heard him tell the story of the Alamo.

Davy Crockett was an ardent American patriot, a gallant frontier soldier who also served in the State Legislature of Tennessee and for three terms in Congress. When Mexico claimed the territory that is now the state of Texas, he joined the nation's armed forces in its defense. He lost his life at the Alamo in San Antonio on March 6, 1836. The ending of his account of the Alamo is characteristic of him:

"Go ahead! Liberty and independence forever!"

The Alamo

by Davy Crockett

I write this on the nineteenth of February, 1836, at
San Antonio. We are all in high spirits, though we
are rather short of provisions, for men who have ap-
petites that could digest any thing but oppression.
But no matter, we have a prospect of soon getting
our bellies full of fighting, and that is victuals and
drink to a true patriot any day. We had a little sort
of convivial party last evening: just about a dozen
of us set to work, to see whether we could not get rid
of that curse of the land, whisky, and we made considerable progress. But my poor friend Thimblerig
got sewed up just about as tight as the eyelet-hole
in a lady's corset, and a little tighter too, I reckon.
For when he went to bed he called for a boot-jack,
which was brought to him, and he bent down on
his hands and knees, and very gravely pulled off his
hat with it, for the darned critter was so thoroughly
swiped that he didn't know his head from his heels.

But this wasn't all the folly he committed: he pulled off his coat and laid it on the bed, and then hung himself over the back of a chair; and I wish I may be shot if he didn't go to sleep in that position. Seeing the poor fellow completely used up, I carried him to bed, and he knew nothing about what occurred until I told him the next morning.

This morning I saw a caravan of about fifty mules passing by Bexar, and bound for Santa Fe. They were loaded with different articles to such a degree that it was astonishing how they could travel at all, and they were nearly worn out by their labours. They were without bridle or halter, and yet proceeded with perfect regularity in a single line. And the owners of the caravan rode their mustangs with their enormous spurs, weighing at least a pound a piece, with rowels an inch and a half in length, and lever bits of the harshest description, able to break the jaws of their animals under a very gentle pressure. The men were dressed in the costume of Mexicans. Colonel Travis sent out a guard to see that they were not laden with munitions of war for the enemy. I went out with the party. The poor mules were bending under a burden of more than three hundred pounds, without including the panniers, which were bound so tight as almost to stop the breath of the poor animals. Each of the sorrowful line came up, spontaneously, in turn to have his girth unbound and his load removed. They seemed scarcely able to keep upon their feet, and as they successively obtained relief, one after another heaved a long and deep sigh, which it was painful to hear, because it proved that the poor brutes had been worked beyond their strength. What a world of misery man inflicts upon the rest of creation in his brief passage through life!

Finding that the caravan contained nothing intended for the enemy, we assisted the owners to replace the heavy burdens on the backs of the patient but dejected mules, and allowed them to pursue their weary and lonely way. For full two hours we could see them slowly winding along the narrow path, a faint line that ran like a thread through the extended prairie. Finally they were whittled down to the little end of nothing in the distance and were blotted out from the horizon.

The caravan had no sooner disappeared than one of the hunters, who had been absent several days, came in. He was one of those gentlemen who don't pride themselves much upon their costume, and reminded me of a covey who came into a tavern in New York when I was last in that city. He was dressed in five jackets, all of which failed to conceal his raggedness, and as he bolted in, he exclaimed:

"Worse than I look! But no matter, I've let myself for fourteen dollars a month, and find my own prog and lodging."

"To do what?" demanded the barkeeper.

"To stand at the corner for a paper-mill sign — 'cash for rags' — that's all. I'm about to enter upon the stationery business, you see." He tossed off his grog, and bustled out to begin his day's work.

But to return to the hunter. He stated that he had met some Indians on the banks of the Rio Frio, who informed him that Santa Anna, with a large force, had already crossed the Neuces, and might be expected to arrive before San Antonio in a few days. We immediately set about preparing to give him a warm reception, for we are all well aware, if our little band is overwhelmed by numbers, there is little mercy to be expected from the Mexicans — it is war to the knife.

I jocosely asked the ragged hunter, who was a smart, active young fellow, of the steamboat and alligator breed, whether he was a rhinoceros or a hyena, as he was so eager for a fight with the invaders. "Neither the one, nor t'other, Colonel," says he, "but a whole menagerie in myself. I'm shaggy as a bear, wolfish about the head, active as a cougar, and can grin like a hyena, until the bark will curl off a gum log. There's a sprinkling of all sorts in me, from the lion down to the skunk. And before the war is over you'll pronounce me an entire zoological institute, or I miss a figure in my calculation. I promise to swallow Santa Anna without gagging, if you will only skewer back his ears, and grease his head a little."

He told me that he was one in the fatal expedition fitted out from New Orleans, in November last, to join the contemplated attack upon Tampico by Mehia and Peraza. They were, in all, about one hundred and thirty men, who embarked as emigrants to Texas. And the terms agreed upon were, that it was optional whether the party took up arms in defence of Texas, or not, on landing. They were at full liberty to act as they pleased. But the truth was, Tampico was their destination, and an attack on that city the covert design, which was not made known before land was in sight. The emigrants were landed, some fifty, who doubtless had a previous understanding, joined the standard of General Mehia, and the following day a formidable fort surrendered without an attack. The whole party were now tendered arms and ammunition, which even those who had been decoyed accepted. And, the line being formed, they commenced the attack upon the city.

The hunter continued: "On the 15th of November our little army, consisting of one hundred and fifty men, marched into Tampico, garrisoned by two thousand Mexicans, who were drawn up in battle array in the public square of the city. We charged them at the point of the bayonet, and although they so greatly outnumbered us, *in two minutes* we completely routed them. They fled, taking refuge on the house tops, from which they poured a destructive fire upon our gallant little band. We fought them until daylight, when we found our number decreased to fifty or sixty broken-down and disheartened men. Without ammunition, and deserted by the officers, twenty-eight immediately surrendered. But a few of us cut our way through, and fortunately escaped to the mouth of the river, where we got on board a vessel and sailed for Texas.

"The twenty-eight prisoners wished to be considered as prisoners of war. They made known the manner in which they had been deceived, but they were tried by a court-martial of Mexican soldiers, and condemned to be shot on the fourteenth day of December, 1835, which sentence was carried into execution."

After receiving this account from my new friend, the old pirate and the Indian hunter came up, and they went off together, and I went to see a wild

Mexican hog, which one of the hunters had brought in. These animals have become scarce, which circumstance is not to be deplored, for their flesh is of little value. And there will still be hogs enough left in Mexico, from all I can learn, even though these should be extirpated.

February 22. The Mexicans, about sixteen hundred strong, with their President Santa Anna at their head, aided by Generals Almonte, Cos, Sesma, and Castrillon, are within two leagues of Bexar. General Cos, it seems, has already forgot his parole of honour, and is come back to retrieve the credit he lost in this place in December last. If he is captured a second time, I don't think he can have the impudence to ask to go at large again without giving better bail than on the former occasion. Some of the scouts came in, and brought reports that Santa Anna has been endeavoring to excite the Indians to hostilities against the Texians, but so far without effect. The Cumanches, in particular, entertain such hatred for the Mexicans, and at the same time hold them in such contempt, that they would rather turn their tomahawks against them, and drive them from the land, than lend a helping hand. We are up and doing, and as lively as Dutch cheese in the dog-days. The two hunters that I have already introduced to the reader left the town, this afternoon, for the purpose of reconnoitring.

February 23. Early this morning the enemy came in sight, marching in regular order, and displaying their strength to the greatest advantage, in order to strike us with terror. But that was no go; they'll find that they have to do with men who will never lay down their arms as long as they can stand on their legs. We held a short council of war, and, finding that we should be completely surrounded, and over-whelmed by numbers, if we remained in the town, we concluded to withdraw to the fortress of Alamo, and defend it to the last extremity. We accordingly filed off, in good order, having some days before placed all the surplus provisions, arms, and am-munition in the fortress. We have had a large national flag made. It is composed of thirteen stripes, red and white, alternately, on a blue ground with a large white star, of five points, in the centre, and between the points the letters TEXAS. As soon as all our little band, about one hundred and fifty in number, had entered and secured the fortress in the best possible manner, we set about raising our flag on the battlements; on which occasion there was no one more active than my young friend, the bee hunter. He had been all along sprightly, cheerful, and spirited, but now, notwithstanding the control that he usually maintained over himself, it was with difficulty that he kept his enthusiasm within bounds. As soon as we commenced raising the flag he burst forth, in a clear, full tone of voice, that made the blood tingle in the veins of all who heard him:

Up with your banner, Freedom,
  Thy champions cling to thee;
They'll follow where'er you lead 'em,
  To death, or victory; —
Up with your banner, Freedom.

Tyrants and slaves are rushing
  To tread thee in the dust;
Their blood will soon be gushing,
  And stain our knives with rust; —
But not thy banner, Freedom.

While stars and stripes are flying,
  Our blood we'll freely shed;
No groan will 'scape the dying,
  Seeing thee o'er his head; —
Up with your banner, Freedom.

This song was followed by three cheers from all within the fortress, and the drums and trumpets commenced playing. The enemy marched into Bexar, and took possession of the town, a blood-red flag flying at their head, to indicate that we need not expect quarter if we should fall into their clutches. In the afternoon a messenger was sent from the enemy to Colonel Travis, demanding an unconditional and absolute surrender of the garrison, threatening to put every man to the sword in case of refusal. The only answer he received was a cannon shot, so the messenger left us with a flea in his ear, and the Mexicans commenced firing grenades at us, but without doing any mischief. At night Colonel Travis sent an express to Colonel Fanning, at Goliad, about three or four days' march from this place, to let him know that we are besieged. The old pirate volunteered to go on this expedition, and accordingly left the fort after nightfall.

February 24. Very early this morning the enemy commenced a new battery on the banks of the river, about three hundred and fifty yards from the fort, and by afternoon they amused themselves by firing at us from that quarter. Our Indian scout came in this evening, and with him a reinforcement of thirty men from Gonzales, who are just in the nick of time to reap a harvest of glory; but there is some prospect of sweating blood before we gather it in. An accident happened to my friend Thimblerig this afternoon. He was intent on his eternal game of thimbles, in a somewhat exposed position, while the enemy were bombarding us from the new redoubt. A three-ounce ball glanced from the parapet and struck him on the breast, inflicting a painful but not dangerous wound. I extracted the ball, which was of lead, and recommended to him to drill a hole through it, and carry it for a watch seal.

"No," he replied, with energy, "may I be shot six times if I do; that would be making a bauble for an idle boast. No, Colonel, lead is getting scarce, and I'll lend it out at compound interest. Curse the thimbles!" he muttered, and went his way, and I saw no more of him that evening.

February 25. The firing commenced early this morning, but the Mexicans are poor engineers, for we haven't lost a single man, and our outworks have sustained no injury. Our sharpshooters have brought down a considerable number of stragglers at a long shot. I got up before the peep of day, hearing an occasional discharge of a rifle just over the place where I was sleeping, and I was somewhat amazed to see Thimblerig mounted alone on the battlement, no one being on duty at the time but the sentries.

"What are you doing there?" says I. "Paying my debts," says he, "interest and all."

"And how do you make out?" says I.

"I've nearly got through," says he; "stop a moment, Colonel, and I'll close the account."

He clapped his rifle to his shoulder, and blazed away, then jumped down from his perch, and said, "That account's settled; them chaps will let me play out my game in quiet next time." I looked over the wall, and saw four Mexicans lying dead on the plain. I asked him to explain what he meant by paying his debts, and he told me that he had run the grape shot into four rifle balls, and that he had taken an early stand to have a chance of picking off stragglers. "Now, Colonel, let's go take our bitters," said he; and so we did.

The enemy have been busy during the night, and have thrown up two batteries on the opposite side of the river. The battalion of Matamoras is posted there, and cavalry occupy the hills to the east and on the road to Gonzales. They are determined to surround us, and cut us off from reinforcement, or the possibility of escape by a sortie. Well, there's one thing they cannot prevent: we'll still go ahead, and sell our lives at a high price.

February 26. Colonel Bowie has been taken sick from overexertion and exposure. He did not leave his bed to-day until twelve o'clock. He is worth a dozen common men in a situation like ours. The bee hunter keeps the whole garrison in good heart

with his songs and his jests, and his daring and determined spirit. He is about the quickest on the
trigger, and the best rifle shot we have in the fort.
I have already seen him bring down eleven of the
enemy, and at such a distance that we all thought it
would be waste of ammunition to attempt it. His
gun is first-rate, quite equal to my Betsey, though
she has not quite as many trinkets about her. This
day a small party sallied out of the fort for wood and
water and had a slight skirmish with three times
their number from the division under General Sesma. The bee hunter headed them and beat the
enemy off, after killing three.

On opening his Bible at night, of which he always reads a portion before going to rest, he found
a musket ball in the middle of it. "See here, Colonel," said he, "how they have treated the valued
present of my dear little Kate of Nacogdoches."

"It has saved your life," said I.

"True," replied he, more seriously than usual,
"and I am not the first sinner whose life has been
saved by this book." He prepared for bed, and before retiring he prayed, and returned thanks for his
providential escape; and I heard the name of Kate
mingled in his prayer.

February 27. The cannonading began early this
morning, and ten bombs were thrown into the fort,

but fortunately exploded without doing any mischief. Provisions are becoming scarce, and the enemy are endeavoring to cut off our water. If they attempt to stop our grog in that manner, let them look out, for we shall become too wrathy for our shirts to hold us. We are not prepared to submit to an excise of that nature, and they'll find it out. This discovery has created considerable excitement in the fort.

February 28. Last night our hunters brought in some corn and hogs, and had a brush with a scout from the enemy beyond gun-shot of the fort. They put the scout to flight, and got in without injury. They bring accounts that the settlers are flying in all quarters, in dismay, leaving their possessions to the mercy of the ruthless invader, who is literally engaged in a war of extermination, more brutal than the untutored savage of the desert could be guilty of. Slaughter is indiscriminate, sparing neither sex, age, nor condition. Buildings have been burnt down, farms laid waste, and Santa Anna appears determined to verify his threat and convert the blooming paradise into a howling wilderness. For just one fair crack at that rascal, even at a hundred yards distance, I would bargain to break my Betsey, and never pull trigger again. My name's not Crockett if I wouldn't get glory enough to appease my stomach for the remainder of my life.

The scouts report that a settler, by the name of Johnson, flying with his wife and three little children, when they reached the Colorado, left his family on the shore, and waded into the river to see whether it would be safe to ford with his wagon. When about the middle of the river he was seized by an alligator, and, after a struggle, was dragged under the water, and perished. The helpless woman and her babes were discovered, gazing in agony on the spot, by other fugitives who happily passed that way, and relieved them. Those who fight the battles experience but a small part of the privation, suffering and anguish that follow in the train of ruthless war. The cannonading continued, at intervals, throughout the day, and all hands were kept up to their work. The enemy, somewhat imboldened, draws nigher to the fort. So much the better. There was a move in General Sesma's division toward evening.

February 29. Before daybreak we saw General Sesma leave his camp with a large body of cavalry and infantry, and move off in the direction of Goliad. We think that he must have received news of Colonel Fanning's coming to our relief. We are all in high spirits at the prospect of being able to give the rascals a fair shake on the plain. This business of being shut up makes a man wolfish. I had a little brush this morning before breakfast. The enemy had planted a piece of ordnance within gun-shot of the fort during the night, and the first thing in the morning they commenced a brisk cannonade, point-blank, against the spot where I was snoring. I turned out pretty smart, and mounted the rampart. The gun was charged again, a fellow stepped forth to touch her off, but before he could apply the match I let him have it, and he keeled over.

A second stepped up, snatched the match from the hand of the dying man, but Thimblerig, who had followed me, handed me his rifle, and the next instant the Mexican was stretched on the earth beside the first. A third came up to the cannon, my companion handed me another gun, and I fixed him off in like manner. A fourth, then a fifth, seized the match, who both met with the same fate, and then the whole party gave it up as a bad job, and hurried off to the camp, leaving the cannon ready charged where they had planted it. I came down, took my bitters, and went to breakfast. Thimblerig told me that the place from which I had been firing was one of the snuggest stands in the whole fort, for he never failed picking off two or three stragglers before breakfast, when perched up there. And I recollect, now, having seen him there, ever since he was wounded, the first thing in the morning, and the last at night, and at times, thoughtlessly playing at his eternal game.

March 1. The enemy's forces have been increasing in numbers daily, notwithstanding they have already lost about three hundred men in the several assaults they have made upon us. I neglected to mention in the proper place, that when the enemy came in sight we had but three bushels of corn in the garrison, but have since found eighty bushels in a deserted house. Colonel Bowie's illness still continues, but he manages to crawl from his bed every day, that his comrades may see him. His presence alone is a tower of strength. The enemy becomes more daring as his numbers increase.

March 2. This day the delegates meet in general convention, at the town of Washington, to frame our Declaration of Independence. That the sacred instrument may never be trampled on by the children of those who have freely shed their blood to establish it, is the sincere wish of David Crockett. Universal independence is an almighty idea, far too extensive for some brains to comprehend. It is a beautiful seed that germinates rapidly, and brings forth a large and vigorous tree, but like the deadly Upas, we sometimes find the smaller plants wither and die in its shades. Its blooming branches spread far and wide, offering a perch of safety to all alike, but even among its protecting branches we find the eagle, the kite, and the owl preying upon the helpless dove and sparrow. Beneath its shade myriads congregate in goodly fellowship, but the lamb and the fawn find but frail security from the lion and the jackal, though the tree of independence waves over them.

Some imagine independence to be a natural charter, to exercise without restraint, and to their fullest extent, all the energies, both physical and mental, with which they have been endowed; and for their individual aggrandizement alone, without regard to the rights of others, provided they extend to all the same privilege and freedom of action. Such independence is the worst of tyranny.

March 3. We have given over all hopes of receiving assistance from Goliad or Refugio. Colonel Travis harangued the garrison, and concluded by exhorting them, in case the enemy should carry the fort, to fight to the last gasp, and render their victory even more serious to them than to us. This was followed by three cheers.

March 4. Shells have been falling into the fort like hail during the day, but without effect. About dusk in the evening, we observed a man running toward the fort, pursued by about half a dozen Mexican cavalry. The bee hunter immediately knew him to be the old pirate who had gone to Goliad, and, calling to the two hunters, he sallied out of the fort to the relief of the old man, who was hard pressed. I followed close after. Before we reached the spot the Mexicans were close on the heels of the old man, who stopped suddenly, turned short upon his pursuers, discharged his rifle, and one of the enemy fell from his horse. The chase was renewed, but finding that he would be overtaken and cut to pieces, he now turned again, and, to the amazement of the enemy, became the assailant in his turn. He clubbed his gun, and dashed among them like a wounded tiger, and they fled like sparrows.

By this time we reached the spot, and, in the ardour of the moment, followed some distance before we saw that our retreat to the fort was cut off by another detachment of cavalry. Nothing was to be done but to fight our way through. We were all of the same mind.

"Go ahead!" cried I, and they shouted, "Go ahead, Colonel!"

We dashed among them, and a bloody conflict ensued. They were about twenty in number, and they stood their ground. After the fight had continued about five minutes, a detachment was seen issuing from the fort to our relief, and the Mexicans scampered off, leaving eight of their comrades dead upon the field. But we did not escape unscathed, for both the pirate and the bee hunter were mortally wounded, and I received a sabre cut across the forehead. The old man died, without speaking, as soon as we entered the fort. We bore my young friend to his bed, dressed his wounds, and I watched beside him. He lay, without complaint or manifesting pain, until about midnight, when he spoke, and I asked him if he wanted anything.

"Nothing," he replied, but drew a sigh that seemed to rend his heart, as he added, "Poor Kate of Nacogdoches!" His eyes were filled with tears, as he continued, "Her words were prophetic, Colonel"; and then he sang in a low voice that resembled the sweet notes of his own devoted Kate,
But toom cam' the saddle, all bluidy to see,
And hame cam' the steed, but hame never cam' he.

He spoke no more, and, a few minutes after died. Poor Kate, who will tell this to thee!

March 5. Pop, pop, pop! Bom, bom, bom! throughout the day. No time for memorandums now. Go ahead! Liberty and independence forever!

[*Here ends Colonel Crockett's manuscript.*]

IN THE
CIVIL WAR
1861-1865

From

Commander-in-Chief of the Union Army, Abraham Lincoln

On March 4, 1865, in his Second Inaugural Address, President Abraham Lincoln said:

"With malice toward none, with charity for all; with firmness in the right, as God gives us to see the right, let us strive on to finish the work we are in; to bind up the nation's wounds; to care for him who shall have borne the battle, and for his widow, and his orphan; to do all which may achieve and cherish a just and lasting peace among ourselves and with all nations."

From

Commander-in-Chief of the Confederate Army, Robert E. Lee

On April 10, 1865, Robert E. Lee said farewell to the Army of Northern Virginia:

"After four years of arduous service, marked by unsurpassed courage and fortitude, the Army of Northern Virginia has been compelled to yield to overwhelming numbers and resources. I need not tell the survivors of so many hard-fought battles, who have remained steadfast to the last, that I have consented to this result from no distrust of them, but, feeling that further valor and devotion could accomplish nothing that could compensate for the loss that would have attended the continuation of the contest, I have determined to avoid the useless sacrifice of those whose past services have endeared them to their countrymen. By the terms of the agreement, officers and men can return to their homes and remain there until exchanged. You will take with you the satisfaction that proceeds from the consciousness of duty faithfully performed; and I earnestly pray that a merciful God will extend to you His blessing and protection. With an increasing admiration of your kind and generous consideration of myself, I bid you an affectionate farewell."

The Secret of
the Seven Days

by James Warner Bellah

The tension eased up a bit after the Cross Keys and
Port Republic fights. Up in the Shenandoah Valley,
on June eighth, Stonewall Jackson met Frémont's
Fed Army at Cross Keys and drove him back on
Harrisonburg — losing poor, gallant Turner Ashby.
The next day Jackson crossed the river at Port
Republic and drove General Shields's army back
up the Luray Valley. Three days later, down Richmond way, General J. E. B. Stuart — the same who
was a lieutenant colonel up at Manassas the year
before — rode his twelve hundred cavalry thundering around McClellan's hundred and five thousand
'sieging army — from Mechanicsville on the north
clear almost to the James River on the south — to
show up the whole Yankee threat for a loose-jointed
heavy hand over Richmond with scant power to
close the fist, now that Robert Edward Lee was in
command.

That was when Davin Ancrum got the letter from his father that if he got anywhere near his Great-aunt Honor Summerhayes's place, he was to drop by for another horse to replace the one he had to shoot. So Davin showed the letter and got a three-day pass to go down Charlottesville way to Aunt Honor's horse farm.

Roan Catlett grinned, "Slack times a three-day pass is good for two weeks, but you come back, y'hear? With Forney Manigault out for wounds, I don't aim to git ridin' orders, without you with me for luck, boy!"

"Well" — Davin waved his pass — "if anything starts, Gin'ral Jackson'll know where to find me. Just tell him to come git me."

It was a bright June day when Davin crossed the Blue Ridge, with heavy heat to come, by the fast way the mists smoked off the treetops after sunrise. He felt free and light in spirit. His own man, for sure. Turned full sixteen with this past year of Valley fighting, but with boy still hiding under it. Funny how that could be. Like two people, almost.

Davin laughed at both. "I sure ain't still goin' to school studying books — whatever else!"

He caught a mule ride halfway up Brown's Gap and a couple of rides in army wagons farther along. A great golden day, getting better to live in each mile east. A day to slowly meet a yellow-haired girl in a pale blue dress, with a silver ribbon to her hair.

Davin met a hearse. Caught up with it rather, a few miles beyond Mechum's River Station. A real old-fashioned hearse with glass sides where they weren't busted out, and lacquered urns and white feather plumes on it, moth-eaten somewhat — like the old white-muzzled jugheads that pulled it. Old Negra on the box; beside him a quartermaster captain in a brand-new uniform frock coat and sword, his arm in a black silk sling. Two soldiers stood below in the road, spitting and waiting like soldiers do, for the next word of what happens.

The captain turned slowly on the box and looked down at Davin walking along. "About time you showed up, trooper. Just follow along. . . . Come on, Neb; tickle 'em up," and the hearse started off again down the dirt road.

Davin looked at the two dusty soldiers. They were about the same height and in the same state of campaign shabbiness that he was. An infantryman and an artilleryman.

The beetle-crusher held out his hand. "Three-whitts' m'name, scout. Thirty-third Virginians. Lousy Thirty-third — but we git to git a bath and spankin' new uniforms, soon's we reach Richmond."

"That so?" Davin said. "Well, I had a bath yesterday, and I don't aim t'go t'Richmond."

"Talk yoreself out of Christmas, wouldn't y', bub? Suppose t'be four of us for funeral escort — infantry, artillery, cav'ry, and we pick up the quartermaster up in Richmond, where they got plenty of them lyin' aroun' loose."

Davin shook his head. "I'm out of Gin'ral Turner Ashby's lot. I got a three-day pass for down Charlottesville way. That's where I'm goin'."

"Look here," Threewhitts winked, "you wouldn't up and spoil a man's fine funeral, now would you, scout?"

"What's it got to do with me?" Davin said. "I got a legal pass."

"Sure, sure," Threewhitts said. "Only Captain Scott Barnaby here'll write you an extension. Got too much other trouble to let you go, now he's got you. Body ain't fresh's it might be. Buried for a time after it happened. Brought an undertaker up from Richmond, but you know how it is, the weather turns warm. Sealed iron casket with a window in it. But the family wants burial in Richmond and the captain's got plenty money on him to see it happens that way. Know any girls in Richmond?"

"Only my Cousin Tandy," Davin said, "but I still ain't agoin'."

The artilleryman jerked his head toward the casket in the hearse. "Brigadier General Chadwick McHoes," he said. "Acting Deputy Quartermaster General of all of Jeff Davis's armies. His hoss blew up on him. M'name's Tom Jourdin. The Revrund Doctor Captain Pendleton's old batt'ry. Just got over wounds."

"His hoss blew up?"

Jourdin said, "Sure did. Shell went right inside the animule. Blew up inside. Wasn't any hoss left and precious little general, they tell."

With that, the three of them walked on silently for a while, trailing the old mule-drawn hearse.

"They got observation balloons for the fightin' down around Richmond," Threewhitts said presently. "I sure aim to see 'em if I can. Read in the papers how. Yanks call theirs the Intrepid. They got a balloon professor who ascends it up with a wire down from it — from over the Chickahominy near Gaines' Mill — to look-see our lines and tell back by telegraph. Got to git up a thousand feet to stay clear of our Whitworth guns south of the river."

"Yo're plumb crazy," Jourdin said. "A thousand feet is way high an' up!"

"We got any?" Davin asked.

"Sort of a one," Threewhitts nodded. "Home-made like. We gas it up in Richmond tied to an engine and run it up and down the York River Railroad to ascend it up our side of the fighting, paper says."

"That's somethin', I reckon," Davin said. "Saw one go up once, Market Fair in Staunton before the war. Fellow hanging on it too. Striped tights."

Wasn't any use arguing this escort thing. Just walk along with it for company and beggar off casually when he got to Aunt Honor's. The only thing was that walking and talking to the two others, the whole escort pulled in under Aunt Honor's side portico and stopped before Davin quite realized where he was.

Aunt Honor Summerhayes was a fixture. Summerhayeses are old people around Charlottesville, and old people tend to breed up fixtures. It won't do her kindly to tell how she looked, but you should see how, to understand. A big woman. Big to tall, that is. Not through. Through, she was no thicker than a thin strong man'd be, any place. Only one better horseman in the whole Commonwealth of Virginia than Miz Honor. Jeb Stuart. Bred horses, Miz Honor. Years of it made her look sort of like a horse, like married people get to look alike. But powerful kind to her people. A great hand for chari-

ty. Took care of all the poor people miles around —
even if it killed them.

"Well, Scott," she said to the captain, "I got your
letter, but you took long enough getting here! Put
the hearse out in the barn for the night and come
in for supper. What are these soldiers doing with
you?"

"Escort, ma'am."

"Not that boy there." Aunt Honor pointed a
bony finger at Davin. "That boy's an Ancrum." She
looked Davin questioningly in the eye for a moment.
"Can't call your name, son," she said, "but you've
got Ancrum blood. Not the Dinwaldie Ancrums,
I'd say. A hand or so higher than the Dinwaldies,
and broader in the withers. I reckon the senator's
line. Over Short Mountain way?"

"That's right, ma'am. M'father wrote I was t'git
a hoss."

"For sure!" Aunt Honor boomed. "Come in,
y'all!"

The captain looked at the hearse. "In the barn,
you said, ma'am?"

"Where else?" Aunt Honor squinted at him hard.
"I've known Chad McHoes since I wore pigtails.
He's all packed and loaded, so there's no need un-
loading — with all the fuss of flowers and charcoal
saucers. Besides, it's bad luck — when you're not

buryin' from the house. Never liked Chad too much anyway. It's his brother Beckwith I'm doing this fer.''

After supper, Aunt Honor took Davin into the house office.

"Lucky you're goin' to Richmond," she said. "You can take Cousin Tandy's silk wedding dress down. I'll wrap it for you, damp-proof. I've got a three-year-old hunter for you, son. Eclipse blood with a strong strain of Bright-eyes too. Been hidin' him from the commandeering —"

"But I'm not — Eclipse blood? C'n I see him, Aunt Honor!"

"The family was at the Spotswood Hotel for a while," Aunt Honor said, "but they've opened the old house again — on Broad Street back of the Governor's Mansion."

"But, ma'am, I'm not —"

"Opened it for Cousin Tandy's wedding. Not rightly theirs, the house. Inherited it from the Linthicums when Uncle Sloane married Miss Sarah Linthicum."

"But, Aunt Honor, this Captain Barnaby has made a mis——"

"Wedding dress is a tradition. Belonged to the Duchesse de Saussure. When Grandfather Cassals

was Secretary of Legation he married her, back in
the 'Thirties. Then Cousin Chastity wore it when
she married that schoolteaching popinjay who died
of a consumption in Natchez."

"I'm trying to tell you, ma'am —"

"Next it went over to your branch when your
sister, Henrietta, married Brainerd Manigault.
Brainerd got killed the other day, they tell me. Your
father sent the dress down here to me — to get it to
Richmond somehow. I reckon you're the somehow.
Senator puts great store on family tradition. Great
store."

"M'father?" Davin said. "He wants it down? Well
— I —"

They loaded the great iron casket on a flatcar
down at Charlottesville Station the next day and
rigged a tent fly over it for shade. Captain Barnaby
paid off the hearse and got blankets for the escort.

The Virginia Central Railroad ran pretty close
to the Yankee right wing on the north, after it left
Noel's Junction heading for Richmond, but they
had jump tracks up there to route cars down the
Richmond, Fredericksburg and Potomac line. The
flatcar with the casket got sidetracked off for supply
trains a couple of times. The three of them settled
to it in soldier boredom, getting food now and then

at the stops. Second morning, when Davin pulled
the blankets off his face, where he was lying with
the bundle of Cousin Tandy's wedding dress for a
pillow, the car was on a siding and stopped. He
could smell city all around — damp stone pave-
ments and the dusty spice smell of horse drays, cin-
dery smoke and the dry breath of pine packing
cases.

It was just coming light. Jourdin was sitting on
the casket, getting ready to pull his boots on.

"Cap'n Barnaby woke me awhile back," he said.
"He's gone up to town to arrange. Got to get the
quartermaster fella to make four for escort, and
borry a gun caisson from some defense batt'ry."

Threewhitts yawned and sat up. Davin rolled the
blankets and looped the bundle of Cousin Tandy's
wedding dress across his shoulders with the rope
he'd rigged.

"Left half an hour ago, walking," Jourdin said.
"Funeral's supposed to be from St. Paul's Church,
but we got first to tote him up and leave him lay in
state at the Capitol near Eleventh all day for folks
t'see. Then the captain's got to get new uniforms for
us. He's walkin'. Be a right smart time he's gone,
I reckon."

Threewhitts looked around slowly, taking his
bearings. "This yere must be Fourteenth Street

leading over Mayo's Bridge, with the Richmond docks the other side. Y'all smell bacon cookin'?" Threewhitts drew a deep breath and pointed. "Down by the bridge" — and he scrambled fast off the car.

"Can't all go," Davin shook his head. "Somebody's got to stay with the general."

Threewhitts looked at Jourdin. "How then? Match? Two to go first and scout it up for breakfast, then spell the other one to go?"

Davin and Threewhitts walked across the tracks and climbed up the bank to Fourteenth Street where it leads onto the bridge. The other side, below, the bridge-guard relief was cooking in a skillet around a little scrap-wood fire.

They spoke to them and made a deal on account of being out of Ashby's Cavalry and the 33rd Virginians of the Stonewall Brigade. "That so? Well, sure 'nuff. Long way from home, ain't you? Gather 'round."

With his mouth full, sitting on the bridge bank, Davin saw the little steamboat tied up on the far side of the wharves beyond the bridge. Great bubble of bright-colored rags heaped beside it on the dock. Like to smother the steamboat under, if it fell over on it. Like to fall over on it any minute too; because the rag clutter was ruffling up high like something was trying to get out from under — swelling like a great multicolored blister — ballooning.

Davin choked. "There she is, Threewhitts!"

"She's just that freakin' balloon," the guard corporal snorted. "They gassing it up from the dock main. Don't any of them know how to work it, you ask me. Blow th'selves up someday sure."

"What about Tom Jourdin's breakfast?"

"Match you." Davin flipped a coin.

Davin walked down to the dock. They had this thing hooked up to a wheel gas valve beside the mooring, filling it full with a powerful hosing sound and a stench of raw gas you could have hung a blanket roll on. A pile of mismatched silk like a patchwork quilt. The crew on the dock were walking out the great silk folds, keeping them smooth for filling, spreading the rolled part flat and keeping the basket ropes clear from snarling the fishnet that went around the outside.

The sergeant fella with them had a twisted leg that bent outward at the knee, instead of front and back. Quite a trick for him to walk with it, so he stood mostly, shouting how.

"Howdy, bub." He looked at Davin. "Never saw one of these yere contraptions before, I reckon?"

"Yes, I did," Davin said. "Up at Staunton Market Fair three years ago, I saw one."

"Saw me, then" — the sergeant nodded. "Made m'living at it. Ascended up at Staunton, three years ago."

"Striped tights?" Davin asked.

"Striped tights," the sergeant nodded solemnly. "The Miraculous Wizard Watts, Professor of Applied Aeronautics."

"That's something!" Davin said. "You goin' up now?"

"Nope." Watts shook his head. "Busted m'leg at Philadelphia right after Staunton," and he pointed at his knee, flexing it so Davin could see how it worked. "Besides, they got a cav'ry lieutenant fer that — who can draw on the map what he sees. Lieutenant Barraclough."

Davin nodded. "Balloon at Staunton was all one color — silver. How comes it this one's like a rainbow?"

Wade snorted. "This yere's a project. When they got the idea we had to have a balloon to match the Yanks, they don't have silk to make one. What'd they do? Collected ev'ry silk dress from ev'ry girl fer miles around! Come on, lay off your blanket bundle and give us a hand here" — and he bent quickly to the snarling net ropes, feeding them back to Davin to lay clear.

"It ain't m'blanket bundle. It's my Cousin Tandy's wedding" — and then with sudden mountain shrewdness — "present," he said, and snugged the end of the bundle tight under his arm. "Well," he said, "I reckon I better mosey."

Sergeant Watts straightened up. "Say, wait a minute." Davin gripped the bundle tighter. "Where you from? You ain't a Richmond soljer."

"Ashby's Cav'ry, up in the Valley. Leastwise Ashby's until he got killed. Don't know whose now."

"It's true then, ain't it?" Watts fixed him with an intent eye. "About General Jackson being in Richmond last night, conferencing with General Lee?"

"I — don't know. Just got in t'day m'self. Gin'ral Jackson was bivouacked at Madison's Cove up in the Valley when I left three days ago. How could he be here?"

"You're here, ain't you?" Watts pursed his lips. "So could Jackson be. He moves around, they tell," and he laughed. "You ain't lyin'?"

Davin shook his head, but there was a vague unrest upon him suddenly. It didn't set right now, to be so far away from his outfit. Out of hand of news from people he knew, and things he had learned to feel instinctively for true or false. The lost-dog feeling of soldiers on their own.

"They goin' up soon's it's full?" he asked awkwardly.

"That's why I asked you. We been ascending before by running her down the York River Railroad on an engine. Now we got these orders to hook her up to this yere steamboat and run her down the James."

"That so? What's down the James to look at? McClellan's army's up the north between Mechanicsville and White Oak Swamp," Davin said.

"That's just it. Ain't nothin' down the James. Yankee gunboats near Bermuda Hundred and transports at City Point is all."

"What then?"

"Well" — Watts winked — "if I was a Yank and seen this balloon go up down the James to look-see, I'd get itchy about what for. It'd draw my attention why it ain't up north side around the Chickahominy where it always was before. Wouldn't it you? Like mebbe we want 'em to think we're gettin' set to hit 'em down the James side."

"So they pull a lot of reserves down to prepare against it. That yore idea?"

Sergeant Watts shrugged. "Why not? If Stonewall Jackson was in Richmond last night, his Valley army may be right behind. He hits the Feds north in the Mechanicsville flank and keeps 'em movin' toward the James till they're rolled clean up on themselves, right to left, like a parlor rug, come spring cleaning!"

The unease in Davin stirred again. He turned and looked back the way he had come. Threewhitts and Jourdin were nowhere in sight. There was some distant artillery firing way up to the north, but not hot. Just then half a dozen folds each side of the main balloon bubble caught the gas full, and rippled into the rising mass of silk, swelling it high above them, with the rope net snarling again under their feet so they had to jump clear.

There was this Lieutenant Barraclough yelling now for everybody to give a hand, and Davin grabbed hold with the rest of the crew. They drew the covering net clear of its tangle and rove out the shrouds of basket ropes, walking them down aboard the steamboat to where the basket lay on the after-deck beside the anchor-rope winch. You could feel the silk bag begin to tug now. Lot of force in the gas and coming in fast.

"Get up topside, some of you fellas!" Watts yelled. "Fend her clear the funnel before a spark catches her!" Somebody on shore screaming, "Fend her off the trees!" and everybody was running around, some on the lower deck with axes were cutting the mooring ropes and the man at the gas valve was turning the wheel frantically, like a brakeman on a runaway steam car.

The balloon made a noise inside like a great drum booming once, muffled, and it swelled suddenly full round, drawing the net snug and jerking the shroud lines taut. The basket, on its side on the deck, jerked up to sit on its bottom, spewing out sandbags and glasses and a map board. Then the man at the valve snaffled the gas neck tight with a strap and unhooked it free of the pipe. With that the bag leaped straight up aft of the steamer to the limit of the anchor rope, carrying the basket with it until the bottom of it was four feet above the deck with the snubbed anchor rope drumming like a bull-fiddle string — and the steamer in midstream, its engine throbbing.

A cut of panic knifed through Davin at sight of the water between him and shore, but like all things in the army you can't do anything about, it left nothing but the determination that they still wouldn't get Cousin Tandy's wedding dress to put with the extras in the patch bin forward, against rips and tears. Absent without leave you could talk away or take the punishment, but this wedding dress his father —

They had the sandbags gathered together to re-rig on the basket rim and Lieutenant Barraclough stood with the map board and glasses while half a dozen men tried to wind down the winch to bring the basket back to deck. They were coming around the bend now, with the Navy yard left, heading south down the James toward Drewry's Bluff. Davin couldn't just stand there, so he turned to help, building up credit for himself against a letdown, which was his usual way. Winch would let out, but they couldn't get it to grind down.

"Give somebody a leg up!" Watts yelled. "Then hand him the sandbags; that'll weight it!"

A dozen of them had their hands up, clawing at the basket, Davin with them. They looked at one another and one made a hand stirrup. "Come on, son," and before Davin really knew he was doing it, he put his foot in and they hoicked him high enough to grab the basket rim and tumble headfirst inside. When he got his head over, they began to pass up the sandbags.

Lieutenant Barraclough handed up the map board and field glasses. "There's racks for them," he said, and just as he said it, the winch ratchet let go in a running metallic shriek and the basket shot thirty feet up and stuck again.

It knocked Davin flat inside and took the breath

out of him. When he got his head over the rim that time, the thirty feet was not only up but it was aft as well, over the steamer's muddy wake.

Lieutenant Barraclough stood in the stern, shouting at him through cupped hands, "Sit tight! Don't try to slide down the rope!"

Then for half an hour they worked on the winch, sweating and hammering and cursing it, while Davin watched them, and the steamboat plowed on toward Drewry's Bluff.

The lieutenant kept calling to him off and on. Finally he said, "Look, trooper. We can't grind you down, and if you slide down the rope, I can't get up to observe. We can head back in and call it off or we can let you up farther, for you to do the observing. Which'll it be?"

"Well, I don't know, sir. I ain't never —"

"That toggle to the hoop above you is the rip cord. If you go all the way up, you can pull that to let the gas out and bring you down. Coming down, if it's too fast, you dump out sand."

Davin frowned. "Yes, I know — but —"

"All you do is look for dust on the roads to indicate troop movement," Barraclough shouted, "and mark the map! It's the Gilmer map. Nine sixteenths of an inch to the mile. You're a cavalryman. It's just like horse scouting, only from higher up!"

"How — far — up — is higher up?" Davin shouted.

"That's Drewry's Bluff ahead, left." Barraclough pointed. "High enough only for you to see well over north and as far east as City Point. Higher if they shoot!"

"Higher if they — what?"

And just then the ratchet began to hammer shrill again, the men at the winch leaped back, shouting, and the balloon bounded upward with a jerk that knocked Davin flat again and a rush of air that gagged him. When he finally got his head over the rim that time, the steamboat was a tiny toy way below and the whole James River no wider than a farm ditch. His face frozen in fear, he hung on for a few minutes, his eyes tight shut, pulling up on the basket rim. The basket was turning slowly as the gasbag turned, but after a few minutes it came steady and he opened his eyes, and suddenly it was the most amazing thing in the whole wide world, and the pure exhilaration of it drenched his soul in awful beauty.

He could see way east and north now — miles, when he used the field glasses.

Must be fourteen miles to the Yankee right wing at Mechanicsville Bridge. Couldn't get to make that out for sure, but he could sure enough see the Chickahominy and White Oak Swamp six or seven miles northeast, where McClellan had his left wing secured. Then suddenly in the high silence, he heard distant artillery fire. He put the glasses north to try to see the red of shell bursts in the haze, but it was still too far. Up Mechanicsville way.

"By glory, mebbe Stonewall Jackson has sneaked down to help jasperoo them, and I'm missing it!" he said aloud.

He came in closer with the glasses and caught a line of light blue ammunition wagons raising a long plume of dust toward where the Long Bridge Road joins with Willis Church. Marked them down on the map. Over east between Crenshaw's and where Western Run crosses, there was a column of infantry marching north. Low dust, thick-clouded. Two regiments anyway, by the column length — moving toward the gunfire. He marked them down. Then it got so easy it made him chuckle. Just like hossback scouting, except you could see everything. Cavalry moving north out of W. M. Harrison's Landing — high dust and thin, and four artillery batteries turning left at the sawmill near Mt. Prospect.

He was so excited he shouted down what he was seeing, even though it was way too far to hear. He could see the steamboat, tiny as a water bug, well south of Drewry's Bluff now, with the rippled wake out back and the bow wave front, like swimming legs. He went back to his work, spotting more dust moving north on the roads, all the while the artillery fire way up there got hotter and heavier, like the long roll on distant drums.

"Sure is a big battle making! It must be Gin'ral Jackson's come down from the Valley! It must be — and I'm missing it!" he cried.

That time, when he looked down at the steamboat, there was no wake or bow wave to her and she was canted around sideways to the river current, tipped slightly to her port side with the tug of the balloon rope on her stern. Grounded hard on a sand bar. The rope trailed east straight across the river and the Yankee side of the bank, with the wind that pressured the bag. Smoke puffs there were, from the riverbanks, like rifle fire and, by Garry, it was rifle fire — with a platoon of blue coats scrambling down the banks to get closer range on the steamer. The wind caught the bag hard now and tugged the anchor rope almost straight, carrying the basket over farther inland. They'd sure enough capture the steamboat, caught as she was on the bar; then they'd capture him. No blessed fear, they'd capture him!

For a white moment of panic, he tried to remember exactly what the lieutenant had told him. Let sand out to go higher; pull the rip cord to come down. He pulled Cousin Tandy's wedding-dress bundle tighter around his shoulder, clutched the map board and pulled on the rip cord. Nothing happened for a moment, except the basket seemed to drift farther inland on the anchor rope. Drifting, it brought the ground closer up to him. He pulled harder and, looking back, found he could no longer see the river, only little blue figures running from it. There were trees coming up fast toward him now, so he pulled a few sandbag dump cords. That slowed the trees, but not too much, for a moment later he could see the leaves on them. Then the anchor rope was slicing into them, snipping leaves in a green cloud behind. Then the basket plowed into top branches and the great silk bubble went on ahead and settled, rippling out flat like a great spread crazy quilt.

Davin got out fast, fell a bit, and began to climb down. He could hear distant shouting from the direction of the James, and a few scattered rifle shots. So he headed off in the opposite direction, going fast toward the north by the sun. Came to the edge of the woods and saw a farm wagon moving along, direction of Long Bridge Road. Piled high with last fall's hay. Crawled in back for a breather and to put distance between him and the Yanks, without leaving trail.

After the better part of a slow hour, the road ran
through woods again, so Davin dropped down from
the hay and crawled in under the bushes to think it
out. He could still hear the heavy artillery firing to
the far north of him. He had no clear idea of what
time it was, but he was dead solid in his mind now
that it must be Stonewall Jackson up there. It must
be, from the sharp and ugly character of the fight,
and all that Watts had said.

He climbed a tree after a while and listened out
the firing carefully. It sure was somewhere up
around Mechanicsville. He figured from the map, if,
like Watts said, McClellan began to roll up like a
rug under Jackson's pressure and get forced down
across the Chickahominy toward the James, that
it'd be on a route down — something like — Mechanicsville, Gaines' Mill, Cold Harbor, Savage Station, Frayser's Farm, Malvern Hill, because that's
the way the roads lay. Having decided that, he went
to sleep for the rest of daylight, because if McClellan
was coming down that way, that would be the best
way for Davin to get north to join his own outfit.
And night would be the best time to work his way
through a hundred and five thousand Yankees.

That night he worked north as far as a place on
his map called Tate & Riddell. Quite a road net
joined there — Charles City Road, Long Bridge,

Quaker Road — with connecting short roads across. Holed up to sleep the day off in a clump of rhododendrons, he couldn't sleep much because of Yankee troop movements all day. Passed the time by putting all of it on his map — infantry, cavalry, artillery — just as he'd been told to do in the balloon. But close to, this way, he could get the regimental numbers from the flags and what states they were from and approximately what time they passed, with arrows in which direction they were moving. It built up to quite a thing after a while, that maybe some general could use right handily.

The firing kept moving east for the three days Davin worked slow toward it; until the twenty-eighth it was up north of Savage Station on the Richmond and York River Railroad. Davin was getting a right decent span of mileage, considering he had to move slowly to avoid countersigns at night. But then, so was General Jackson getting good mileage, in spite of the fact he had to fight a hundred thousand Feds for it. Whatever, Stonewall Jackson and Davin were right close to joining up now, and as Davin holed up at sunup in a clump of maple on the Seven Mile Road, the whole character of the Yankee rear movement began to change. First, there were wounded wagonloads pulling out south. So many of them you could hardly keep count. A three-day slug-fight crop. Mechanicsville, Gaines' Mill, Old Cold Harbor wounded. Then there were regiments marching back. Badly mauled regiments, with batteries down to three guns, two, and sometimes only one. Horse cavalry with half the men afoot and straggling. Then heavy supply wagons. Ammunition, flour barrels, pork and tentage. Engineers with bridge equipment. Everything. And lying roadside in the brush, Davin got all of it on his map.

The Seven Days' Battle caught Davin as it swept past Watkin's Mill, late the afternoon of the twenty-ninth, headed south for Frayser's Farm and Malvern Hill. Taliaferro's third brigade hot on the tail of McClellan pulling out of Savage Station. When you're close, you have to lie close on account of passwords and itchy trigger fingers. Davin waited until he saw the 23rd Virginia colors pass him in the skirmish line across the fields, then he got up and walked in toward the colors of the 10th Virginians moving down the road in reserve.

"Fella says he's out of Ashby's Cav'ry. Talks crazy. Says he came part way by b'loon and his pass run out. Better send him to the provost marshal. . . . Get along, bud; we got work coming up."

The provost said, "Got a map on him, hunh? Balloon? He's daffy! Must be a spy. There's General Jackson's topographical engineer over theah. Take him over to Captain Hotchkiss — mebbe's a major now. Let Hotchkiss decide, I'm busy."

The letdown after three days of working back through the enemy lines had Davin shaky inside by that time. He just stumbled along in a tired daze, like a man who's got his courage up to have the blacksmith pull his tooth — and the tooth's come clean without snagging off the roots. He handed over the map whenever they asked and just stood blinking from lack of sleep, and waiting, with Cousin Tandy's wedding dress still roped to his shoulder.

Young Hotchkiss frowned at him. "Look here," he said; "this is the whole axis of General Jackson's attack marked out, and General Jackson don't even tell his staff! And look here — here's almost the whole of McClellan's army movement behind the lines for the past three days, horse, men and guns. They are pulling out for the James to hold the high ground at Malvern Hill, you ask me! Keep that man close. If he tries to escape, shoot him!"

"I ain't agoin' nowhere," Davin said. "I just come."

Then suddenly across the road, there was Gin'ral Jackson himself, standing by his great horse with his officers grouped around him. White with dust and caked wet in the armpits with sweat through the jacket. His great round beard was scraggled from tugging at it three battle days. His face looked drawn to the bones under it, tight like a pudding cloth, from lack of sleep, but his back was as straight as a ramrod. He took the map from young Hotch-kiss and glanced at it. Then for a moment he studied it intently, fingering out the road nets on it with the hand hit at Manassas — that always throbbed him after. Measuring mileage by laying the first two joints of the index finger to the road, then to the scale. Then, very slowly, he let the map hang to arm's length and he turned and looked south toward the battle thunder rolling down to-ward Frayser's Farm now, and he put his thumb and finger to his old Institute kepi visor where it was burred, and he pulled the hat tight, so's just not to hide the awful blue battle light of his eyes. Then he smiled . . .

Davin didn't find Roan or his own outfit until after the Malvern Hill battle on July first, which left McClellan in full retreat to under his gun-boats' covering fire on the James River. Didn't find him until after he'd got into Richmond again, dur-ing the lull.

In Richmond at the Summerhayes house on

Broad Street behind the Governor's Mansion, Davin gave the dress to his Cousin Tandy.

"Oh, Davin, we've been expecting you!" she said. "Aunt Honor's got a three-year-old hidden out in our stable here for you. Eclipse blood." When Davin gave her the dress she said, "How perfectly sweet of you! You're a dear boy, but I can't possibly wear it!"

"Why not, Tandy? Don't it fit?"

"But it's not that at all! You just don't know Richmond girls, Davin. They just live and breathe this awful war in every fiber!"

"That so?"

"Of course it's so. How could we live if we weren't patriotic to the last drop of our blood! You see, they collected every silk dress in the Confederacy to make a balloon, and it got captured!"

"Oh, it did?"

"And no Richmond girl would ever think of wearing a silk —"

When he found Roan, Roan squinted at him hard. "Well, Dav," he said, "Gin'ral Jackson sure knew where to find you. He sure came and got you!"

"I didn't git to talk to him m'self," Davin said earnestly, "but is there going to be trouble about the pass running out? Can you fix it for me? You know I wouldn't —"

Roan considered it for a moment. "They were all for putting you through the sausage grinder for a spy. Until they put it to Gin'ral Jackson himself."

"Bad trouble?"

"Well," Roan drawled, "it's beyond anything I can do about the pass, if that's what you mean. With them all up in arms about how you got that map and what to do with you, Old Stonewall Jackson made the decision himself."

"What'd he say? Come on! Tell me!"

"Well," Roan said, "Stonewall just sort of smiled at them in that way he has, and handed them back the pass. Then he got on his horse, with your map in hand and 'Gentlemen,' he said, 'extend the man's pass!' "

A Horseman in the Sky

by Ambrose Bierce

One sunny afternoon in the autumn of the year 1861 a soldier lay in a clump of laurel by the side of a road in western Virginia. He lay at full length upon his stomach, his feet resting upon the toes, his head upon the left forearm. His extended right hand loosely grasped his rifle. But for the somewhat methodical disposition of his limbs and a slight rhythmic movement of the cartridge-box at the back of his belt he might have been thought to be dead. He was asleep at his post of duty. But if detected he would be dead shortly afterward, death being the just and legal penalty of his crime.

The clump of laurel in which the criminal lay was in the angle of a road which after ascending southward a steep acclivity to that point turned sharply to the west, running along the summit for perhaps one hundred yards. There it turned southward again and went zigzagging downward through the forest. At the salient of that second angle was a large flat rock, jutting out northward, overlooking the deep valley from which the road ascended. The rock capped a high cliff; a stone dropped from its outer edge would have fallen sheer downward one thousand feet to the tops of the pines. The angle where the soldier lay was on another spur of the same cliff. Had he been awake he would have commanded a view, not only of the short arm of the road and the jutting rock, but of the entire profile of the cliff below it. It might well have made him giddy to look.

The country was wooded everywhere except at the bottom of the valley to the northward, where there was a small natural meadow, through which flowed a stream scarcely visible from the valley's rim. This open ground looked hardly larger than an ordinary dooryard, but was really several acres in extent. Its green was more vivid than that of the enclosing forest. Away beyond it rose a line of giant cliffs similar to those upon which we were supposed to stand in our survey of the savage scene, and through which the road had somehow made its climb to the summit. The configuration of the valley, indeed, was such that from this point of observation it seemed entirely shut in, and one could but have wondered how the road which found a way out of it had found a way into it, and whence came and whither went the waters of the stream that parted the meadow more than a thousand feet below.

No country is so wild and difficult but men will make it a theater of war. Concealed in the forest at the bottom of that military rat-trap, in which half a hundred men in possession of the exits might have starved an army to submission, lay five regiments of Federal infantry. They had marched all the previous day and night and were resting. At nightfall they would take to the road again, climb to the place where their unfaithful sentinel now slept, and descending the other slope of the ridge fall upon a camp of the enemy at about midnight. Their hope was to surprise it, for the road led to the rear of it. In case of failure, their position would be perilous in the extreme; and fail they surely would should accident or vigilance apprise the enemy of the movement.

2

The sleeping sentinel in the clump of laurel was a young Virginian named Carter Druse. He was the son of wealthy parents, an only child, and had known such ease and cultivation and high living as wealth and taste were able to command in the mountain country of western Virginia. His home was but a few miles from where he now lay.

One morning he had risen from the breakfast table and said, quietly but gravely: "Father, a Union regiment has arrived at Grafton. I am going to join it."

The father lifted his leonine head, looked at the son a moment in silence, and replied: "Well, go, sir, and whatever may occur do what you conceive to be your duty. Virginia, to which you are a traitor, must get on without you. Should we both live to the end of the war, we will speak further of the matter. Your mother, as the physician has informed you, is in a most critical condition. At the best she cannot be with us longer than a few weeks, but that time is precious. It would be better not to disturb her."

So Carter Druse, bowing reverently to his father, who returned the salute with a stately courtesy that masked a breaking heart, left the home of his childhood to go soldiering. By conscience and courage, by deeds of devotion and daring, he soon commended himself to his fellows and his officers. And it was to these qualities and to some knowledge of the country that he owed his selection for his present perilous duty at the extreme outpost. Nevertheless, fatigue had been stronger than resolution and he had fallen asleep. What good or bad angel came in a dream to rouse him from his state of crime, who shall say? Without a movement, without a sound, in the profound silence and the languor of the late afternoon, some invisible messenger of fate touched with unsealing finger the eyes of his consciousness — whispered into the ear of his spirit the mysterious awakening word which no human lips ever have spoken, no human memory ever has recalled. He quietly raised his forehead from his arm and looked between the masking stems of the laurels, instinctively closing his right hand about the stock of his rifle.

His first feeling was a keen artistic delight. On a colossal pedestal, the cliff — motionless at the extreme edge of the capping rock and sharply outlined against the sky — was an equestrian statue of impressive dignity. The figure of the man sat the figure of the horse, straight and soldierly, but with the repose of a Grecian god carved in the marble which limits the suggestion of activity. The gray costume harmonized with its aerial background. The metal of accouterment and caparison was softened and subdued by the shadow; the animal's skin had no points of highlight. A carbine strikingly foreshortened lay across the pommel of the saddle, kept in place by the right hand grasping it at the "grip"; the left hand, holding the bridle rein, was invisible. In silhouette against the sky the profile of the horse was cut with the sharpness of a cameo. It looked across the heights of air to the confronting cliffs beyond. The face of the rider, turned slightly away, showed only an outline of temple and beard. He was looking downward to the bottom of the valley. Magnified by its lift against the sky and by the soldier's testifying sense of the formidableness of a near enemy the group appeared of heroic, almost colossal, size.

For an instant Druse had a strange, half-defined feeling that he had slept to the end of the war and was looking upon a noble work of art reared upon that eminence to commemorate the deeds of an heroic past of which he had been an inglorious part. The feeling was dispelled by a slight movement of the group: the horse, without moving its feet, had drawn its body slightly backward from the verge; the man remained immobile as before. Broad awake and keenly alive to the significance of the situation. Druse now brought the butt of his rifle against his cheek by cautiously pushing the barrel forward through the bushes, cocked the piece, and glancing through the sights covered a vital spot of the horseman's breast. A touch upon the trigger and all would have been well with Car-

ter Druse. At that instant the horseman turned his
head and looked in the direction of his concealed
foeman — seemed to look into his very face, into
his eyes, into his brave, compassionate heart.

Is it then so terrible to kill an enemy in war — an
enemy who has surprised a secret vital to the safety
of one's self and comrades — an enemy more formidable for his knowledge than all his army for its
numbers? Carter Druse grew pale.

He shook in every limb, turned faint, and saw
the statuesque group before him as black figures,
rising, falling, moving unsteadily in arcs of circles
in a fiery sky. His hand fell away from his weapon,
his head slowly dropped until his face rested on the
leaves in which he lay. This courageous gentleman
and hardy soldier was near fainting from intensity
of emotion.

It was not for long. In another moment his face
was raised from earth, his hands resumed their
places on the rifle, his forefinger sought the trigger.
Mind, heart, and eyes were clear, conscience and
reason sound. He could not hope to capture that
enemy; to alarm him would but send him dashing
to his camp with his fatal news. The duty of the
soldier was plain: the man must be shot dead from
ambush — without warning, without a moment's
spiritual preparation, with never so much as an un-

spoken prayer, he must be sent to his account. But no — there is a hope: he may have discovered nothing — perhaps he is but admiring the sublimity of the landscape. If permitted, he may turn and ride carelessly away in the direction whence he came. Surely it will be possible to judge at the instant of his withdrawing whether he knows. It may well be that his fixity of attention —

Druse turned his head and looked through the deeps of air downward, as from the surface to the bottom of a translucent sea. He saw creeping across the green meadow a sinuous line of figures of men and horses — some foolish commander was permitting the soldiers of his escort to water their beasts in the open, in plain view from a dozen summits!

Druse withdrew his eyes from the valley and fixed them again upon the group of man and horse in the sky, and again it was through the sights of his rifle. But this time his aim was at the horse. In his memory, as if they were a divine mandate, rang the words of his father at their parting: "Whatever may occur, do what you conceive to be your duty." He was calm now. His teeth were firmly but not rigidly closed; his nerves were as tranquil as a sleeping babe's — not a tremor affected any muscle of his body. His breathing, until suspended in the act of taking aim, was regular and slow.

Duty had conquered; the spirit had said to the body: "Peace, be still." He fired.

3

An officer of the Federal force, who in a spirit of adventure or in quest of knowledge had left the hidden bivouac in the valley, and with aimless feet had made his way to the lower edge of a small open space near the foot of the cliff, was considering what he had to gain by pushing his exploration further. At a distance of a quarter-mile before him, but apparently at a stone's throw, rose from its fringe of pines the gigantic face of rock, towering to so great a height above him that it made him giddy to look up to where its edge cut a sharp, rugged line against the sky. It presented a clean, vertical profile against a background of blue sky to a point half the way down, and of distant hills, hardly less blue, thence to the tops of the trees at its base. Lifting his eyes to the dizzy altitude of its summit the officer saw an astonishing sight — a man on horseback riding down into the valley through the air!

Straight upright sat the rider, in military fashion, with a firm seat in the saddle, a strong clutch upon the rein to hold his charger from too impetuous a plunge. From his bare head his long hair streamed upward, waving like a plume. His hands were concealed in the cloud of the horse's lifted mane. The animal's body was as level as if every hoofstroke encountered the resistant earth. Its motions were those of a wild gallop, but even as the officer looked they ceased, with all the legs thrown sharply forward as in the act of alighting from a leap. But this was a flight!

Filled with amazement and terror by this apparition of a horseman in the sky, the officer was overcome by the intensity of his emotions; his legs failed him and he fell. Almost at the same instant he heard a crashing sound in the trees — a sound that died without echo — and all was still.

The officer rose to his feet, trembling. The familiar sensation of an abraded shin recalled his dazed faculties. Pulling himself together he ran rapidly, obliquely away from the cliff to a point distant from its foot. Thereabout he expected to find his man; and thereabout he naturally failed. In the fleeting instant of his vision his imagination had been so wrought upon the apparent grace and ease and intention of the marvelous performance that it did not occur to him that the line of march of aerial cavalry is directly downward, and that he could find the objects of his search at the very foot of the cliff. A half-hour later he returned to camp.

This officer was a wise man; he knew better than to tell an incredible truth. He said nothing of what he had seen. But when the commander asked him if in his scouting he had learned anything of advantage to the expedition he answered:

"Yes, sir; there is no road leading down into this valley from the southward."

The commander, knowing better, smiled.

4

After firing his shot, Private Carter Druse reloaded his rifle and resumed his watch. Ten minutes had hardly passed when a Federal sergeant crept cautiously to him on hands and knees. Druse neither turned his head nor looked at him, but lay without motion or sign of recognition.

"Did you fire?" the sergeant whispered.

"Yes."

"At what?"

"A horse. It was standing on yonder rock — pretty far out. You see it is no longer there. It went over the cliff."

The man's face was white, but he showed no other sign of emotion. Having answered, he turned away his eyes and said no more. The sergeant did not understand.

"See here, Druse," he said, after a moment's silence, "it's no use making a mystery. I order you to report. Was there anybody on the horse?"

"Yes."

"Well?"

"My father."

The sergeant rose to his feet and walked away. "Good God!" he said.

IN THE
SPANISH-AMERICAN
WAR
1898

From
Colonel Theodore Roosevelt

Theodore Roosevelt was appointed Assistant Secretary of the Navy by President McKinley in 1897. But when war broke out with Spain in 1898, he resigned and was commissioned a colonel in the U.S. Army. Roosevelt organized a volunteer cavalry group that became known as the Rough Riders whom he led in the now famous charge up San Juan Hill in Cuba.

About Cuba, he said in 1899:

"Cuba, in my judgment, is entitled to settle for itself whether it shall be an independent state or an integral portion of the mightiest of republics. But until order and stable liberty are secured, we must remain in the island to insure them, in protecting all alike, and yet in showing proper recognition to the men who have fought for Cuban Liberty."

The Lone Charge of William B. Perkins

by Stephen Crane

He could not distinguish between a five-inch
quick-firing gun and a nickle-plated ice-pick, and
so, naturally, he had been elected to fill the position
of war correspondent. The responsible party was
the editor of the Minnesota *Herald*. Perkins had no
information of war, and no particular rapidity of
mind for acquiring it, but he had that rank and fi-
brous quality of courage which springs from the
thick soil of Western America.

It was morning in Guantánamo Bay. If the marines encamped on the hill had had time to turn
their gaze seaward, they might have seen a small
newspaper despatch-boat wending its way toward
the entrance of the harbor over the blue, sunlit
waters of the Caribbean. In the stern of this tug
Perkins was seated upon some coal bags, while the
breeze gently ruffled his greasy pajamas. He was

staring at a brown line of entrenchments sur-
mounted by a flag, which was Camp McCalla. In
the harbor were anchored two or three grim, gray
cruisers and a transport. As the tug steamed up the
radiant channel, Perkins could see men moving
on shore near the charred ruins of a village. Perkins was deeply moved. Here already was more war
than he had ever known in Minnesota. Presently
he, clothed in the essential garments of a war correspondent, was rowed to the sandy beach. Marines
in yellow linen were handling an ammunition supply. They paid no attention to the visitor, being
morose from the inconveniences of two days and
nights of fighting. Perkins toiled up the zigzag
path to the top of the hill, and looked with eager
eyes at the trenches, the field-pieces, the funny little
Colts, the flag, the grim marines lying wearily on
their arms. And still more, he looked through the
clear air over one thousand yards of mysterious
woods from which emanated at inopportune times
repeated flocks of Mauser bullets.

Perkins was delighted. He was filled with admiration for these jaded and smoky men who lay so
quietly in the trenches waiting for a resumption of
guerilla enterprise. But he wished they would heed
him. He wanted to talk about it. Save for sharp inquiring glances, no one acknowledged his existence.

Finally he approached two young lieutenants, and in his innocent Western way he asked them if they would like a drink. The effect on the two young lieutenants was immediate and astonishing. With one voice they answered, "Yes, we would." Perkins almost wept with joy at this amiable response, and he exclaimed that he would immediately board the tug and bring off a bottle of Scotch. This attracted the officers, and in a burst of confidence one explained that there had not been a drop in camp. Perkins lunged down the hill, fled to his boat, and then toiled again up the hill in the blasting sun with his enthusiasm in no ways abated. The parched officers were very gracious, and such was the state of mind of Perkins that he did not note properly how serious and solemn was his engagement with the whiskey. And because of this fact, there happened the lone charge of William B. Perkins.

Now, as Perkins went down the hill, something happened. A private in those high trenches found that a cartridge was clogged in his rifle. It then becomes necessary with most kinds of rifles to explode the cartridge. The private took the rifle to his captain, and explained the case. But it would not do in that camp to fire a rifle for mechanical purposes and without warning, because the eloquent sound

would bring six hundred tired marines to tension
and high expectancy. So the captain turned, and in
a loud voice announced to the camp that he found
it necessary to shoot into the air. The communication rang sharply from voice to voice. Then the
captain raised the weapon and fired. Whereupon —
and whereupon — a large line of guerillas lying in
the bushes decided swiftly that their presence and
position were discovered, and swiftly they volleyed.

In a moment the woods and the hills were alive
with the crack and sputter of rifles. Men on the
warships in the harbor heard the old familiar flut-
flut-fluttery-fluttery-flut-flut-flut from the entrenchments. Incidentally the launch of the *Marblehead*,
commanded by one of our headlong American en-
signs, streaked for the strategic woods like a gallop-
ing marine dragoon, peppering away with its
blunderbuss in the bow.

Perkins had arrived at the foot of the hill, where
began the arrangement of one hundred fifty marines
that protected the short line of communications between the main body and the beach. These men
had all swarmed into line behind fortifications
improvised from the boxes of provisions. And to
them were gathering naked men who had been
bathing, naked men who arrayed themselves speed-
ily in cartridge belts and rifles. The woods and the

hills went flut-flut-flut–fluttery-fluttery-flut-flllllut-tery-flut. Under the boughs of a beautiful tree lay five wounded men thinking vividly.

And now it befell Perkins to discover a Spaniard in the bush. The distance was some five hundred yards. In a loud voice he announced his perception. He also declared hoarsely, that if he only had a rifle, he would go and possess himself of this particular enemy. Immediately an amiable lad shot in the arm said: "Well, take mine." Perkins thus acquired a rifle and a clip of five cartridges.

"Come on!" he shouted. This part of the battalion was lying very tight, not yet being engaged, but not knowing when the business would swirl around to them.

To Perkins they replied with a roar. "Come back here, you fool. Do you want to get shot by your own crowd? Come back!"

As a detail, it might be mentioned that the fire from a part of the hill swept the journey upon which Perkins had started.

Now behold the solitary Perkins adrift in the storm of fighting, even as a champagne jacket of straw is lost in a great surf. He found it out quickly. Four seconds elapsed before he discovered that he was an almshouse idiot plunging through hot, crackling thickets on a June morning in Cuba. Sss-sswing-sing-ing-pop went the lightning-swift metal grasshoppers over him and beside him. The beauties of rural Minnesota illuminated his conscience with the gold of lazy corn, with the sleeping green of meadows, with the cathedral gloom of pine forests. Sshsh-swing-pop!

Perkins decided that if he cared to extract himself from a tangle of imbecility he must shoot. The entire situation was that he must shoot. It was necessary that he should shoot. Nothing would save him but shooting. It is a law that men thus decide when the waters of battle close over their minds. So with a prayer that the Americans would not hit him in the back nor the left side, and that the Spaniards would not hit him in the front, he knelt like a supplicant alone in the desert of chaparral, and emptied his magazine at his Spaniard before he discovered that the Spaniard was a bit of dried palm branch.

Then Perkins flurried like a fish. His reason for being was a Spaniard in the bush. When the Spaniard turned into a dried palm branch, he could no longer furnish himself with one adequate reason.

Then did he dream frantically of some anthracite hiding-place, some profound dungeon of peace where blind mules live placidly chewing the far-gathered hay.

Sss-swing-win-pop! Prut-prut-prrrut! Then a field-gun spoke. *Boom*-ra-swow-ow-ow-ow-*pum*. Then a Colt automatic began to bark. Crack-crk-crk-crk-crk-crk endlessly. Raked, enfiladed, flanked, surrounded, and overwhelmed, what hope was there for William B. Perkins of the Minnesota *Herald?*

But war is a spirit. War provides for those that it loves. It provides sometimes death and sometimes a singular and incredible safety. There were few ways in which it was possible to preserve Perkins. One way was by means of a steamboiler.

Perkins espied near him an old, rusty steamboiler lying in the bushes. War only knows how it was there, but there it was, a temple shining resplendent with safety. With a moan of haste, Perkins flung himself through that hole which expressed the absence of the steam-pipe.

Then ensconced in his boiler, Perkins comfortably listened to the ring of a fight which seemed to be in the air above him. Sometimes bullets struck their strong, swift blow against the boiler's sides, but none entered to interfere with Perkin's rest.

Time passed. The fight, short anyhow, dwindled to prut . . . prut . . . prut-prut . . . prut. And when the silence came, Perkins might have been seen cautiously protruding from the boiler. Presently he strolled back toward the marine lines with his hat

not able to fit his head for the new bumps of wis-
dom that were on it.

The marines, with an annoyed air, were settling
down again when an apparitional figure came from
the bushes. There was great excitement.

"It's that crazy man," they shouted, and as
he drew near they gathered tumultuously about
him and demanded to know how he had accom-
plished it.

Perkins made a gesture, the gesture of a man
escaping from an unintentional mud-bath, the gesture of a man coming out of battle, and then he
told them.

The incredulity was immediate and general. "Yes,
you did! What? In an old boiler? An old boiler?
Out in that brush? Well, we guess not."

They did not believe him until two days later,
when a patrol happened to find the rusty boiler,
relic of some curious transaction in the ruin of the
Cuban sugar industry. The patrol then marveled at
the truthfulness of war correspondents until they
were almost blind.

Soon after his adventure Perkins boarded the tug,
wearing a countenance of poignant thoughtfulness.

Marines Signalling under Fire at Guantánamo

by Stephen Crane

They were four Guantánamo marines, officially known for the time as signalmen, and it was their duty to lie in the trenches of Camp McCalla, that faced the water, and, by day, signal the *Marblehead* with a flag, and, by night, signal the *Marblehead* with lanterns. It was my good fortune — at that time I considered it my bad fortune, indeed — to be with them on two of the nights when a wild storm of fighting was pealing about the hill. And, of all the actions of the war, none were so hard on the nerves, none strained courage so near the panic point, as those swift nights in Camp McCalla. With a thousand rifles rattling; with the field-guns booming in your ears; with the diabolic Colt automatic clacking; with the roar of the *Marblehead* coming from the bay, and, last, with Mauser bullets sneering always in the air a few inches over one's head, and with this enduring from dusk to dawn, it is extremely doubtful if any one who was there will be able to forget it easily. The noise; the impenetrable darkness; the knowledge from the sound of the bullets that the enemy was on three sides of the camp; the infrequent bloody stumbling and death of some man with whom, perhaps, one had messed two hours previous; the weariness of the body, and the more terrible weariness of the mind, at the endlessness of the thing, made it wonderful that at least some of the men did not come out of it with their nerves hopelessly in shreds.

But, as this interesting ceremony proceeded in the darkness, it was necessary for the signal squad to coolly take and send messages. Captain McCalla always participated in the defense of the camp by raking the woods on two of its sides with the guns of the *Marblehead*. Moreover, he was the senior officer present, and he wanted to know what was happening. All night long the crews of the ships in the bay would stare sleeplessly into the blackness toward the roaring hill.

The signal squad had an old cracker-box placed on top of the trench. When not signalling they hid the lanterns in this box. But as soon as an order to

send a message was received, it became necessary
for one of the men to stand up and expose the
lights. And then — oh, my eye — how the guerillas
hidden in the gulf of night would turn loose at
those yellow gleams!

Signalling in this way is done by letting one lantern remain stationary — on top of the cracker-box,
in this case — and moving the other over to the left
and right and so on in the regular gestures of the
wig-wagging code. It is a very simple system of night
communication, but one can see that it presents
rare possibilities when used in front of an enemy
who, a few hundred yards away, is overjoyed at
sighting so definite a mark.

How, in the name of wonders, those four men
at Camp McCalla were not riddled from head to
foot and sent home more as repositories of Spanish
ammunition than as marines is beyond all com-
prehension. To make a confession — when one of
these men stood up to wave his lantern, I, lying in
the trench, invariably rolled a little to the right or
left, in order that, when he was shot, he would not
fall on me. But the squad came off scathless, despite
the best efforts of the most formidable corps in the
Spanish army — the Escuadra de Guantánamo. That
it was the most formidable corps in the Spanish
army of occupation has been told me by many Span-

ish officers and also by General Menocal and other insurgent officers. General Menocal was Garcia's chief-of-staff when the latter was operating busily in Santiago province. The regiment was composed solely of *practicos*, or guides, who knew every shrub and tree on the ground over which they moved.

Whenever the adjutant, Lieutenant Draper, came plunging along through the darkness with an order — such as: "Ask the *Marblehead* to please shell the woods to the left" — my heart would come into my mouth, for I knew then that one of my pals was going to stand up behind the lanterns and have all Spain shoot at him.

The answer was always upon the instant: "Yes, sir." Then the bullets began to snap, snap, snap at his head while all the woods began to crackle like burning straw. I could lie near and watch the face of the signalman, illumed as it was by the yellow shine of lantern light, and the absence of excitement, fright, or any emotion at all on his countenance was something to astonish all theories out of one's mind. The face was in every instance merely that of a man intent upon his business, the business of wig-wagging into the gulf of night where a light on the *Marblehead* was seen to move slowly.

These times on the hill resembled, in some days, those terrible scenes on the stage — scenes of intense gloom, blinding lightning, with a cloaked devil or assassin or other appropriate character muttering deeply amid the awful roll of the thunder-drums. It was theatric beyond words: one felt like a leaf in this booming chaos, this prolonged tragedy of the night. Amid it all one could see from time to time the yellow light on the face of a preoccupied signalman.

Possibly no man who was there ever before understood the true eloquence of the breaking of the day. We would lie staring into the east, fairly ravenous for the dawn. Utterly worn to rags, with our nerves standing on end like so many bristles, we lay and watched the east — the unspeakably obdurate and slow east. It was a wonder that the eyes of some of us did not turn to glass balls from the fixity of our gaze.

Then there would come into the sky a patch of faint blue light. It was like a piece of moonshine. Some would say it was the beginning of daybreak; others would declare it was nothing of the kind. Men would get very disgusted with each other in these low-toned arguments held in the trenches. For my part, this development in the eastern sky destroyed many of my ideas and theories concerning the dawning of the day. But then I had never before had occasion to give it such solemn attention.

This patch widened and whitened in about the speed of a man's accomplishment if he should be in the way of painting Madison Square Garden with a camel's hair brush. The guerillas always set out to whoop it up about this time, because they knew the occasion was approaching when it would be expedient for them to elope. I, at least, always grew furious with this wretched sunrise. I thought I could have walked around the world in the time required for the old thing to get up above the horizon.

One midnight, when an important message was to be sent to the *Marblehead,* Colonel Huntington came himself to the signal place with Adjutant Draper and Captain McCauley, the quartermaster. When the man stood up to signal, the colonel stood beside him. At sight of the lights, the Spaniards performed as usual. They drove enough bullets into that immediate vicinity to kill all the marines in the corps.

Lieutenant Draper was agitated for his chief. "Colonel, won't you step down, sir?"

"Why, I guess not," said the gray old veteran in his slow, sad, always-gentle way. "I am in no more danger than the man."

"But, sir —" began the adjutant.

"Oh, it's all right, Draper."

So the colonel and the private stood side to side and took the heavy fire without either moving a muscle.

Day was always obliged to come at last, punctuated by a final exchange of scattering shots. And the light shone on the marines, the dumb guns, the flag. Grimy yellow face looked into grimy yellow face, and grinned with weary satisfaction. Coffee!

Usually it was impossible for many of the men to sleep at once. It always took me, for instance, some hours to get my nerves combed down. But then it was great joy to lie in the trench with the four signalmen, and understand thoroughly that that night was fully over at last, and that, although the future might have in store other bad nights, one could never escape from the prison-house which we call the past.

At the wild little fight at Cusco there were some splendid exhibitions of wig-wagging under fire. Action began when an advanced detachment of marines under Lieutenant Lucas with the Cuban guides had reached the summit of a ridge overlooking a small valley where there was a house, a well, and a thicket of some kind of shrub with great broad, oily leaves. This thicket, which was perhaps an acre in extent, contained the guerillas. The valley was open to the sea. The distance from the top of the ridge to the thicket was barely two hundred yards.

The *Dolphin* had sailed up the coast in line with the marine advance, ready with her guns to assist in any action. Captain Elliott, who commanded the two hundred marines in this fight, suddenly called out for a signalman. He wanted a man to tell the *Dolphin* to open fire on the house and the thicket. It was a blazing, bitter hot day on top of the ridge with its shriveled chaparral and its straight, tall cactus plants. The sky was bare and blue, and hurt like brass. In two minutes the prostrate marines were red and sweating like so many hull-buried stokers in the tropics.

Captain Elliott called out:

"Where's a signalman? Who's a signalman here?"

A red-headed "mick" — I think his name was Clancy — at any rate, it will do to call him Clancy — twisted his head from where he lay on his stomach pumping his Lee, and, saluting, said that he was a signalman.

There was no regulation flag with the expedition, so Clancy was obliged to tie his blue polkadot neckerchief on the end of his rifle. It did not

make a very good flag. At first Clancy moved a ways
down the safe side of the ridge and wig-wagged
there very busily. But what with the flag being so
poor for the purpose, and the background of ridge
being so dark, those on the *Dolphin* did not see it.
So Clancy had to return to the top of the ridge and
outline himself and his flag against the sky.

The usual thing happened. As soon as the Spaniards caught sight of this silhouette, they let go like
mad at it. To make things more comfortable for
Clancy, the situation demanded that he face the
sea and turn his back to the Spanish bullets. This
was a hard game, mark you — to stand with the
small of your back to volley firing. Clancy thought
so. Everybody thought so. We all cleared out of his
neighborhood. If he wanted sole possession of any
particular spot on that hill, he could have it for all
we would interfere with him.

It cannot be denied that Clancy was in a hurry.
I watched him. He was so occupied with the bullets
that snarled close to his ears that he was obliged to
repeat the letters of his message softly to himself.
It seemed an intolerable time before the *Dolphin*
answered the little signal. Meanwhile, we gazed at
him, marveling every second that he had not yet
pitched headlong. He swore at times.

Finally the *Dolphin* replied to his frantic gesticulation, and he delivered his message. As his part of the transaction was quite finished — whoop! — he dropped like a brick into the firing line and began to shoot; began to get "hunky" with all those people who had been plugging at him. The blue polka-dot neckerchief still fluttered from the barrel of his rifle. I am quite certain that he let it remain there until the end of the fight.

The shells of the *Dolphin* began to plough up the thicket, kicking the bushes, stones, and soil into the air as if somebody was blasting there.

Meanwhile, this force of two hundred marines and fifty Cubans and the force of — probably — six companies of Spanish guerillas were making such an awful din that the distant Camp McCalla was all alive with excitement. Colonel Huntington sent out strong parties to critical points on the road to facilitate, if necessary, a safe retreat, and also sent forty men under Lieutenant Magill to come up on the left flank of the two companies in action under Captain Elliott. Lieutenant Magill and his men had crowned a hill which covered entirely the flank of the fighting companies, but when the *Dolphin* opened fire, it happened that Magill was in the line of the shots. It became necessary to stop the *Dolphin* at once. Captain Elliott was not near

Clancy at this time, and he called hurriedly for another signalman.

Sergeant Quick arose, and announced that he was
a signalman. He produced from somewhere a blue
polka-dot neckerchief as large as a quilt. He tied it
on a long, crooked stick. Then he went to the top
of the ridge, and turning his back to the Spanish
fire, began to signal to the *Dolphin*. Again we gave
a man sole possession of a particular part of the
ridge. We didn't want it. He could have it and wel-
come. If the young sergeant had had the smallpox,
the cholera, and the yellow fever, we could not
have slid out with more celerity.

As men have said often, it seemed as if there
was in this war a God of Battles who held His
mighty hand before the Americans. As I looked
at Sergeant Quick wig-wagging there against the
sky, I would not have given a tin tobacco-tag for
his life. Escape for him seemed impossible. It
seemed absurd to hope that he would not be hit.
I only hoped that he would be hit just a little, little,
in the arm, the shoulder, or the leg.

I watched his face, and it was as grave and serene
as that of a man writing in his own library. He was
the very embodiment of tranquillity in occupation.
He stood there amid the animal-like babble of the
Cubans, the crack of rifles, and the whistling snarl

of the bullets, and wig-wagged whatever he had to wig-wag without heeding anything but his business. There was not a single trace of nervousness or haste.

To say the least, a fight at close range is absorbing as a spectacle. No man wants to take his eyes from it until that time comes when he makes up his mind to run away. To deliberately stand up and turn your back to a battle is in itself hard work. To deliberately stand up and turn your back to a battle and hear immediate evidences of the boundless enthusiasm with which a large company of the enemy shoot at you from an adjacent thicket is, to my mind at least, a very great feat. One need not dwell upon the detail of keeping the mind carefully upon a slow spelling of an important code message.

I saw Quick betray only one sign of emotion. As he swung his clumsy flag to and fro, an end of it once caught on a cactus pillar, and he looked sharply over his shoulder to see what had it. He gave the flag an impatient jerk. He looked annoyed.

IN THE
FIRST
WORLD WAR

1914-1918

From

Commander-in-Chief Woodrow Wilson

"It is a fearful thing to lead this great peaceful people into war, into the most terrible and disastrous of all wars, civilization itself seeming to be in the balance. But the right is more precious than peace, and we shall fight for the things which we have always cherished nearest to our hearts — for democracy, for the right of those who submit to authority to have a voice in their own governments, for the dominion of right by such a concert of free peoples as shall bring peace and safety to all nations and make the world itself at last free."

Spoken on April 12, 1917,
in President Wilson's war message to Congress

Fear

by James Warner Bellah

It was a little spot, that fear, but it had ached in his heart for months — ever since his first solo flight at Upavon Aerodrome. It had come suddenly one morning like the clean pink hole of a steel-jacketed bullet — a wound to be ashamed of, a wound to fight against, a wound that never quite healed. Always it was there to throb and to pinch like the first faint gnawing of cancer. It came with him to the theater and rankled his mind: "Enjoy this — it may be your last play." It crept into his throat at meals sometimes, and took away the poor savor that was left to the foods of wartime.

The fear of the men who fly. Sometimes he pictured it as an imp — an imp that sat eternally on his top plane and questioned him on the strength of rudder wires, pointed to imaginary flaws in struts, suggested that petrol was low in the tank, that the engine would die on the next climbing turn.

It was with him now as the tender that was to take him up to his squadron jolted and bounced its way across the *pavé* on the outskirts of Amiens. The squadron was the last place he had to go to. All the months that were gone had led up to this. These were the wars at last. This was the place he would cop it, if he was to cop it at all.

He shrugged. Anyway, he had had his four days in London and his ten days idling at Pilot's Pool before the squadron sent for him. He braced one shoulder against the rattling seat and reached in his tunic pocket for a cigarette. Mechanically he offered one to the driver. The man took it with a grubby finger.

"Thankee, sor-r."

He nodded and lighted both cigarettes with the smudge of his pocket lighter. Anyway, he was not flying up to 44. That was one flight saved. Funny, that fear — how it came and went like the throb of a nerve in an open tooth. Sometimes the spot was large, and filled his whole being. Then again it would shrink to a dull ache, just enough to take the edge from the beauty of the sunrise and the sparkle from the wine of the moon.

There had been a time when it had jumped in every fiber of his soul. He had been a cadet officer then, with only twelve solo hours in the air, under the old rough-and-tumble system of learning to fly. Spinning at that time was an unsolved mystery to him, a ghastly mystery that had meant quick death in a welter of blood, flecked with splinters. Fred McCloud had gone that way, and Johnny Archamboult. For weeks afterward, Johnny's screams had rung in his ears like a stab of pain, until the mere smell of petrol and fabric dope made the fear crawl into his throat and strangle him. Somehow he had kept on with the rest, under the merciless scourge that lashed one on to fly — and the worst fear of seeing cold scorn in the eyes of the men who taught the lore of thin cloud miles.

The tender twisted and dodged along the hard mud ribbon that ran like a badly healed cicatrix across the pock-scarred face of the fields. Gnarled and bleak, they were fields that had held the weight of blood-crazed men — still held them in unmarked graves, where they had fallen the year before under the steel flail. He had heard stories from his older brother about those fields — the laughing brother who had gone away one day and returned months later without his laugh, only to go away again, not to come back. He had seen pictures in the magazines — But somehow no one had caught their utter bleakness as he saw it now.

The riven boles of two old trees crouched and

argued about it on the lead-gray horizon, tossing their splintered arms and shrieking, he fancied, like quarreling old women in the lesser streets of a village. Close to the roadway, there were a torn shoe and a tin hat flattened like a crushed derby. Poor relics that even salvage could see no further use in. Farther off, a splintered caisson pointed three spokes of a shattered wheel to the sky, like a mutilated hand thrown out in agony. He was seeing it for himself now.

No one could smile at the cleanness of his uniform again and say: "Wait till you get out. When I was in France —" He was out himself now. In a day or so he would go over the line with loaded guns. His instructors at the training 'drone — thin-jawed men with soiled ribbons under their wings — had done no more, and some of them had done less. The thought braced him somewhat. They had seemed so different — so impossible to imitate — those men. Their war had always been a different one from his; a war peopled with vague, fearless men like Rhodes-Moorehouse and Albert Ball and Bishop, the Canadian; men who flew without a thought for themselves.

It occurred to him with a start that theirs was the same war as his now. Twenty-five miles ahead of him, buried somewhere in rat runs, between Bapaume and Cambrai, it went on and on, waiting for him to come — waiting to claw and maim and snuff him out when he did come. It had seemed so far away from him in England. When he was at ground school he had seen it as a place where one did glorious things — he was young, pitifully young — a place that one came back from with ribbons under one's wings, with nice clean scratches decently bandaged. And he had been slightly offended at his brother's attitude — at the things his brother had said of the staff. Then he had gone to Upavon to learn to fly. He had soloed for the first time, and the spot of fear had crawled into his own heart.

They were rattling into the broken streets of a tottering town — a town that leered at them and grimaced through blackened gaps in its once white walls. There was a patched-up estaminet with a tattered yellow awning that tried bravely to smile.

"Albert," said the driver.

The new pilot nodded. Some sapper officers were loitering in the doorways of the café. Their uniforms were faded to a rusty brown and reinforced with leather at the cuffs and elbows. Their buttons were leather, too, to save polishing, and their badges were a dull bronze. He looked down at his white bedford-cord breeches and the spotless skirts of his fur collared British warm — privileges of the flying corps that men envied. Baths, clean clothing, and better food. The P.B.I.'s idea of heaven. They called flyers lucky for their privileges and cursed them a little bit for their dry beds, miles behind the line.

The new pilot wondered if they knew what it meant to be alone in the stabbing cold with no one to talk to, no one to help you, nothing between you and the ground save a thin, trembling fabric of cloth and wire and twenty thousand feet of emptiness. That was his fear — emptiness — nothingness — solitude. Those men under the awning could die in company. Not so himself — alone, screaming into the cloud voids, with no one to hear, no one to help, staring with glazed eyes and foam-flecked lips at the emptiness into which one hurtled to death miles below. The price one paid for a bath! He remembered seeing Grahame-White fly at Southport before the war. People had called him an intrepid aviator. The new pilot laughed harshly inside his throat and stared out across the bare fields.

The car topped a slight rise and turned sharply to the left. The driver pointed his grubby finger. "They be comin' in from afternoon patrol," he said. "Yonder is aerodrome."

There were three flat canvas hangars painted a dull brown, and a straggling line of rusty tin huts

facing them from across the narrow landing space —
like a deserted mining village, shabby and unkempt.
As he watched, he saw the last machine of the afternoon patrol bank at a hundred and fifty feet and
side-slip down for its landing. In his heart he could
hear the metal scream of wind in the flying wires.
A puff of black smoke squirted out in a torn stream
as the pilot blipped on his engine for one more
second before he came into the wind and landed.
By the time the tender rolled up to the dilapidated
squadron office, the machine had taxied into the
row of hangars and the pilot was out. A thin acrid
smell of petrol and carbonized castor oil still hung
in the quiet air between the shabby huts. Snow
in large wet flakes commenced to fall slowly, steadily.

The new pilot climbed down from the tender,
tossed his shoulder haversack beside his kit-bag,
and pushed open the door of the squadron office.
The adjutant was sitting on his desk top, smoking
and talking to someone in a black leather flying
coat and helmet — someone with an oil-streaked face
and fingers still blue and clumsy from the cold.

"Paterson, sir, G. K., Second Lieutenant, re-
porting in from Pilot's Pool for duty with the 44th."

The adjutant raised a careless finger in acknowl-
edgment. "Oh yes. How do? Bring your log books?"

"Yes, sir."

"Chuck 'em down. D'ye mind?"

Paterson laid them upon the desk top, still standing to attention. The adjutant smiled. "Break off," he said. "We're careless here. This isn't cadet school."

The new pilot smiled and relaxed. "Very good, sir."

"That's better," said the adjutant; "makes me feel more comfortable. Just give me a note of yourself now." He reached for a slip of paper. "G. K. Paterson, Two Lt. Next of kin?" Paterson gave his father's name. "Age?"

"Eighteen and four-twelfths."

"Good!" said the adjutant. "You'll find an empty cubicle in B Block — that's the middle line of huts. You're lucky. Roof only leaks in three places. I'll have your duffel trekked over shortly."

The man in the flying coat blew upon his numbed fingers and smiled. "I'm Hoyt," he said. "Skipper of C Flight. I'm going to take you now, before A gets after you." He turned to the adjutant. "That's all right, isn't it, Charlie? Tell 'em I intimidated you." He grinned.

The adjutant shrugged. "Right-o!"

"Come on," said Hoyt. "I'm in your hut block. I'll show you your hole."

They went out into the snow flurry. Mechanics were fussing in little knots around the five tiny machines that had just landed, lining them up, refilling them, and trundling them into the brown musty hangars.

"Le Rhône Camels," said Hoyt. "We've just been over around Cambrai taking a look-see."

Inside one of the hangars, as they passed, Paterson saw something that drew a thin, wet gauze across his eyeballs. On a rough bench just beside the open flap sat a man with his eyes closed and his lips drawn tightly into a straight bluish line. His flying coat was rolled up behind his head for a pillow, and his tunic had been unbuttoned and cut away from his left shoulder. The white of his flesh showed weirdly in the gloom, like the belly of a dead fish. Just below the shoulder, the white was crumpled and reddened as if a clawed paw had been drawn across it. One man was holding his other hand, while another probed and cleaned and dabbed with little puffs of snowy cotton that turned quickly to pink and then to a deep brown.

Hoyt shrugged. "Lucky man. That's Mallory. He was Number Four this afternoon. We never saw a thing. Just happened. Funny." And he smiled. "That's why I was so keen to get you. Can't tell how long it will be before Mallory gets around again, and I've got one vacancy in the flight already." He shrugged. "You'll see a lot of that here — get used to it. It doesn't mean a thing as long as you get back alive."

Paterson looked at him sharply. He wanted to ask him how many didn't get back alive. He wanted to know what had caused the other vacancy in the flight. But people didn't ask those things. People merely nodded casually and went on.

"I suppose not," he said. They tramped on across the aerodrome.

"Here we are," said Hoyt. He kicked open the hut door and groped down the dark passageway, with Paterson after him. Presently he pushed back another door and yanked at a tattered window curtain.

The new pilot saw a tiny room, with two washstands, a cot, a folding chair, and a cracked mirror. In a corner were his kit-bag and haversack. He pulled out his own cot and chair and set them up. Meanwhile Hoyt threw himself down on the other cot. Presently he spoke.

"This is a queer war," he said; "full of queer things, and the queerest of these is charity." He laughed in the darkness. "What was your school?"

"Winchester," said Paterson.

"Right," said Hoyt. "Remember your first day?

This is it over again. They've fed you up on poobah at your training 'drone and down at the Pool. They always do. It's part of the system. Just take it for what it is worth and forget the rest. If you want to know anything, come to me and I'll tell you as well as I can. I've been here three months. When I came, I came just as you did today, pucka green and afraid to the marrow — afraid of uncertainty. You get over that shortly.

"Our job is a funny one, and we're not here for ourselves, and we're not here to be heroes or to get in the newspapers. The V.C.'s are few and far between." He raised himself upon his elbow. "I'm not preaching self-abasement and a greater loyalty to a cause that is right, mind you. I don't know anything about causes or who started the war or why, and I don't care. I'm preaching C Flight and the lives of five men.

"You saw Mallory over at the hangar. It was teamwork that put him there in his own M.O.'s hands. Not much, perhaps"— his finger described a quick arc in the darkness — "just a slight closing in of the formation — a wave of somebody's hand — somebody else dropping back and climbing above him to protect his tail from any stray Huns that might've waylaid him on the way home. That's what I mean. *Esprit de corps* is a cold, hard phrase. Call it what you like. It's the greatest lesson you learn. Never give up a man." Hoyt laughed. "They call me an old woman. Perhaps I am. Take it or leave it.

"Slick up a bit and come into my hutch while I scrape off the outer layer of silt. Dinner in half a tick and I'm filthy as a pig." He vaulted up from the cot and at the door he paused for a moment.

"Ever have wind up?" he asked casually.

Paterson stiffened against the question and the small spot of fear danced within him. "No," he said firmly. Hoyt shrugged. "Lucky man." And he went out into the passageway.

At dinner he met the rest of the squadron and the other men in C Flight. Mallory, very pale, with his arm slung in a soft pad of bandages, sat beside him. They were coming for him later to take him down to the base hospital. Phelps-Barrington sat on the other side of Mallory, mourning the fact that the wound was not his that he might get the inevitable leave to follow. Phelps-Barrington took Paterson's hand with a shrug and asked how Marguerite was in Amiens. "What? You didn't meet Marguerite on your way through? 'Struth!" MacClintock sat across the table beside Hoyt — MacClintock, too young to grow a mustache, but a deep burr that smelled of the heather in the Highlands and huge pink knees under his Seaforth kilts, muscles like the corded roots of an oak. The other man in the flight, Trent, was down with mild flu. He was due back in a week or so from hospital.

There was a wild argument on about the dawn patrol the next morning. Paterson listened to the fragments of talk that flew like saber cuts across the glasses:

"He's in a red tripe. I don't give a damn for Intelligence. Saw him this morning myself. Same machine Mac and I had that brush with down at Péronne."

"The next time they'll get an idea for us to strafe a road clear to Cologne for them. What are we -- street cleaners?"

"So I let go a covey of Coopers and turned for home. They had it spotted for a battery over at 119 Squadron. I saw the pictures. Right pictures, but wrong map squares as usual. That crowd can't tell a battery from a Chinese labor-corps inclosure. I'd rather be a staff officer than a two-seater pilot."

Cruel, thin, casual talk clicking against the teeth in nervous haste; the commercial talk of men bartering their lives against each tick of the clock; men caught like rats in a trap, with no escape but death or a lucky chance like Mallory's. Caught and yet denying the trap — laughing at it until the low roof of the mess shack rumbled with the echo.

Afterward, Hoyt came down the passage with him to his room — Hoyt, with his face cleaned of the afternoon's oil. "We're relieved tomorrow on account of casualties," he said. "I'll tick you out early and we'll go joy riding — see what we can teach each other." He smiled. "Night."

Paterson undressed slowly and threw back the flap of his sleeping bag. He ran his fingers softly down the muscles of his left arm. Automatically they stopped at the spot Mallory had been hit. He stretched his thumb from the arm to his heart — seven inches. He shrugged. Nice to go that way. Clean and quick. He sat upon the edge of his cot and pulled on his pyjama trousers. Oh, well, this was the place — the last place he had to go to. This was the cot he would sleep his last sleep in. If it weren't a lonely job! That chap in the mess who wouldn't be a two-seater pilot for anything. If he could only feel like that. If he could only feel Hoyt's complacency. Hoyt, with his calm smile and the two little ribbons under his wings. Military Cross and the Legion of Honor, and three months before he had been green — pucka green!

Paterson blew out the light and turned in. Hoyt was a good fellow — decent. Outside he could hear Phelps-Barrington's voice muffled by the snow: "Come on, snap into it! Tender for Amiens! Who's coming?" The yell died in the roar from the car's engine.

Paterson lay for a moment thinking. Then suddenly he reached for his pocket flash, snapped it, and stared nervously at the empty cot across the room. There was no bedding on it, nor any kit tucked under it; only the chair beside it, and the cracked mirror.

He got up and padded over in his bare feet. Stenciled on one corner of the canvas there was a name — J. G. H. Lyons. There had been no Lyons introduced to him in the mess. Perhaps he was on leave. Perhaps he had flu with Trent and was down at the base. The spot of fear in his heart trembled slightly and he knew suddenly where J. G. H. Lyons was. He was dead! Somewhere out in the snow, miles across the line, J. G. H. Lyons slept in a shattered cockpit.

The door behind him opened softly. It was Hoyt, in pyjamas. "Got a match?" he asked casually.

Paterson turned sharply and grinned. "Right-o," he said. "There on the table."

Hoyt lighted his pipe. "Can't sleep," he said. "Come in and take Mallory's cot if you want to. I've some new magazines and I can tell you something about our work here until we feel sleepy."

Hoyt was a good fellow.

The cold wet mist lay upon the fields like a soft veil drawn across the face of an old woman who had died in the night. Mechanics, with their balaklavas pulled down across their ears, were running about briskly to keep warm — kicking chocks in front of undercarriage wheels, snapping propellers down with mighty leaps and sweeps until the cold engines barked into life and settled to deep concert roaring. Dust and pebbles, scattered by the backwash, swept into the billowing hangars in a thin choking cloud that pattered against the canvas walls. Hoyt's machine trembled and crept out of the line, with Phelps-Barrington after it. Trent, who had come back from the base the day before, taxied out next.

Paterson waved to the mechanics to pull out his own chocks. They yanked mightily on the ropes, and he blipped his motor with his thumb. Behind him and to the left came Yardley, the new man who had come up from Pool to fill Mallory's place. Then MacClintock, sitting high in his cockpit, rushed out with a roar and a swish of gravel. MacClintock was deputy leader.

Hoyt waved his hand in a quick nervous sweep, and the flight started. Through the mist they roared with their engines howling into sharp echo against the hut walls. A moment later tails whipped up and wheels bounced lightly upon the uneven ground.

Then Hoyt's nose rose sharply and he zoomed into the air in a broad climbing turn, with the five others after him in tight formation.

Paterson glanced at his altimeter — five hundred feet. He looked ahead and to the left. There was Bapaume in its raggedness, half drowned in the mist. Suddenly Phelps-Barrington's machine burst into rose flame and every strut and wire trembled like molten silver — the sun. He could see the red rim just peeping up ahead of him and he was warmer for the sight of it. Below, under the rim of his cockpit, the ground was still wrapped in its gray shroud.

They were climbing up in close formation. The altimeter gave them four thousand feet now. He glanced to the left. Yardley waved. Yardley was going through the agony of his first patrol over the line — the same agony he had gone through himself the week before. Only Yardley seemed different, somehow — surer of himself — less imaginative. He was older, too. Behind them, MacClintock, the watch-dog, was closing in on their tails and climbing above them to be ready to help if the Hun swooped from behind unexpectedly.

There were clouds above — gray blanket clouds that came together in a solid room, with only a torn hole here and there to show the blue. Bad clouds to be under. Hoyt knew it and kept on climbing.

Almost ten thousand feet now. The ground below had cleared slowly and thrown off most of its sullen shroud. Here and there, in depressions, the mist still hung in arabesque ruffles like icing in a confectioner's window or the white smoke of a railway engine.

The line was under them now, running south and east like a jagged dagger cut, in and out, in and out across the land, not stopping for towns, but cleaving straight through their gray smudgy ruins with a cold disregard and a ruthless purpose. The first day he had seen it, it had seemed a dam to him: a breakwater built there to hold something that must not flow past it; a tourniquet of barbed wire twisted and held by half the world that the blood of the other half might not flow. Some day something would break and the whole thing would give way for good or evil. Curiously, now, like Hoyt, he didn't care which. And suddenly he knew how his older brother had felt, on that last leave, and he had called him unsporting in the pride of his youthful heart!

Hoyt was still climbing. Thin wraiths of cloud vapor groped awkwardly for the six tiny Camels, like ghost fingers, trying desperately to stop them and hold them from their work. Paterson glanced again at Yardley. He had been glad when Yardley came. He was still green himself, but Yardley was greener. It helped buck him up to think about it.

The line was behind them now. Hoyt turned south to pass below the anti-aircraft batteries of Cambrai, and presently they crossed the tarnished silver ribbon of the Somme-Scheldt Canal. Mechanically, Paterson reached for his Bowden trigger and pressed it for a burst of ten shots to warm the oil in his Vickers gun against the bite of cold air. Then he clamped the joy-stick between his knees and reached up for the Lewis gun on his top plane.

His throat closed abruptly, with a ghastly dryness, and his knees melted beneath him. The wing fabric beside his gun was ruffling into torn lace and he could see the wood of the camber ribs splintering as he watched! For a moment he was paralyzed, then frantically he whipped around in his seat and swept the air above him. Nothing. There was the torn fabric and the staring rib and nothing else. Mac-Clintock was gone. Yardley was still there, lagging, with the smoke coming in puffs and streaks from his engine. Then Hoyt turned in a wild climb to the left. Phelps-Barrington dipped his nose suddenly and dived with his engine full on, and at once, where there had been only six Camels, the sky was full of gray machines with blunt noses and black crosses.

Blindly he pressed his Bowden trigger and fired into the empty air, blindly he dived after Phelps-Barrington. Somewhere to the left he saw a plume of black smoke with something yellow twisting in the sunlight on its lower end. A blunt nose crossed his propeller — into his stream of bullets. He screamed and banked wildly, still firing. He saw Hoyt above him. He forgot the machine in front and reached for his Lewis to help Hoyt. He tried to wait — something about the outer ring of the rear sight — but his fingers got the better of him and he fired point-blank.

As quickly as it had begun it ended. There was Hoyt circling back, and two other Camels to the left and below him — four of them. They closed in on Hoyt and he wondered where the two others were. He looked for them — probably chasing after the Huns. He could see dots to the southward — too far away to make out the markings. Hoyt had signaled the washout and they were headed back across the line. Funny those two others didn't come. He wondered who they were. Probably Phelps-Barrington and MacClintock, hanging on to the fight until the last. They worked together that way. He had heard them talk in the mess about it. They'd be at it again tonight, and tonight he could join them for the first time. He'd been in a dog fight! Shot and been shot at! The spot of fear shrank to a pinpoint.

The brown smudge of the aerodrome slid over the horizon. He blipped his motor and glided in carefully. No use straining that top wing — no telling what other parts had been hit. No use taking chances.

Hoyt was standing beside his machine with his glove off, staring at his fingernails. Phelps-Barrington was climbing out. Paterson taxied in between them. The man in the fourth machine just sat and stared over the rim of his cockpit. Phelps-Barrington walked slowly across to Hoyt and laid a hand on his shoulder. Hoyt shrugged and stuffed his bare hand into his coat pocket. Paterson sat with his goggles still on and his throat quite dry. The man in the fourth machine vaulted out suddenly, ripped off his helmet and goggles and hurled them to the ground. It was Trent.

He climbed out of his own machine and walked over toward Hoyt. Phelps-Barrington, who had a wild word for all occasions — Phelps-Barrington, who led the night trips to Amiens — was silent. When Paterson came up he shrugged and scowled ferociously.

"Is it you, Pat?" said Hoyt. "Thought it was Yardley."

" 'Struth!" said Phelps-Barrington.

Paterson thrilled as the man slipped an arm through his. For one awful moment he had thought—

"Well," Hoyt said, "those things will happen." And he shrugged again.

"I saw dots to the southward," said Paterson. "Maybe they'll be in later."

"No, little Rollo," said Phelps-Barrington. "They won't be in later or ever. I saw it with my own eyes—both in flames. I thought it was you, and until Trent landed I thought he might be Mac. But I was wrong."

Then suddenly he knew, and his mind froze with the ghastliness of the thought. If he'd been quicker — if he'd turned and climbed above Yardley when he saw him lagging, with the smoke squirting from his hit motor — he could have saved him. If he had kept his eyes open behind instead of dreaming he might have saved MacClintock, too. In a daze, he stumbled after Phelps-Barrington. That's why Trent had hurled his helmet to the ground and walked off. That's why Hoyt had shrugged and said: "Those things will happen." It was his fault — his — Paterson's. He'd bolted and lost his head and fired blindly into the empty air. He hadn't stuck to his man. He had let Yardley drop back alone to be murdered. He wanted to be alone — to think. So quick it had all been.

Phelps-Barrington grabbed his arm and pushed him stumbling into the mess shack. Trent was slumped down at the table with his glass before him, thumbing over a newspaper. He raised his head as they came in and sat down beside him.

Trent looked at Paterson. "Good work, son."

Paterson stared at him in amazement. Trent was going on reading as if he had never stopped. Some time later, Paterson left them and went down to the flight office to find Hoyt. The thought of the morning still bothered him, in spite of Trent's words, and he wanted to clear it up.

"Look here, skipper" Paterson said, "this morning — what about it?"

"What about it?"

"My part — I was fast asleep. I saw Yardley lagging, and I had a moment to cross above him, but I lost my head, I'm afraid, and went wild."

The smile faded and Hoyt laid down his pencil. "Do you really think you could have saved him?"

"He was behind me already when I saw him lagging, just as you climbed and P.-B. dived."

"Then you couldn't have helped him, because Mac was done for when I saw him and climbed, and half a tick after I climbed, P.-B. saw Yardley burst into flames. There you are."

"But if I'd kept my eyes back instead of trusting
to Mac?"

"Look here," said Hoyt, "no man can keep his
eyes on everything. Something always happens in
the place he isn't looking. Bear that in mind and
forget this morning. You've seen a dog fight from
the inside and lived. Take it easy. You're not here
to do everything. You're here to stick to us. You
might have run away. Remember that and be afraid
of it. Remember if you get away by leaving a pal —
he may live to come back. Then you'll have to face
him, and engine trouble is a poor excuse.

"Trouble with you youngsters is that you've been
fed up on poobah. And the myth of the fearless air
fighter. Put it out of your mind. There's no such
thing. Some are less afraid than others. Take your
choice. Class dismissed." Hoyt grinned. "Go get
cleaned up. We'll jog into Amiens for tiffin. Tender
in half an hour. Tell Trent and P.-B."

They spent most of the afternoon with some of
the men from the artillery observation squadron.
For dinner they went to the Du Rhin, and afterward, in another place, there was a fight, as usual,
and chairs crashed like match sticks, until whistles
sounded outside and the A.P.M.'s car, siren screaming, raced up the street. They poured out into the

alleyway and ran, leaving the waiter praying in high, shrieking French.

They rode all the way home singing and shouting to high heaven, forgetting that there were two empty chairs in the mess and that there might be more tomorrow.

Take the cylinders out of my kidneys,
Take the scutcheon pins out of my brain,
Take the cam box from under my backbone
And assemble the engine again!

They roared along like a Juggernaut, with the exhaust splitting the night air. Sometimes they were on the road and sometimes they were off. No one cared so long as they kept hurtling into the darkness.

Phelps-Barrington was fast asleep. Pat woke him up at the aerodrome and tumbled him into the hut.

They stumbled over a kit-bag in the doorway. P.-B. straightened up suddenly. "Good-by, Mac, old lad, sleep tight."

Trent kicked the bag out of the way. "Take P.-B. in with you, Pat. I'm bunking with the skipper. Might have the decency to take Mac's kit over to squadron office and not leave it lying around the passage. 'Night."

Paterson tumbled P.-B. into bed and stood for a

moment at the open window, staring out across the ground mist that billowed knee high in the faint night breeze. He rested his elbows on the sill and hid his face in his trembling hands. If he could only be like the others — casual — calloused. If he had less imagination — more sand — stamina — something. MacClintock had planned this night himself, at breakfast. Yardley had left a letter addressed and stamped on his windowsill.

Paterson's mind jumped miles to the eastward. He saw the two blackened engines lying somewhere in the bleak fields beyond, ploughed into the ground, with their mats of twisted wires coiled around them in a hideous trap.

Their families would get word tomorrow. "Missing," it would read. And then later: "Previously reported missing, now reported killed in action." And tomorrow — perhaps his own family. Why can't it be quick?

The weeks crawled on slowly. Paterson felt like a man climbing a steep ladder. Each day was a rung behind him. Each new rung showed an infinite number still ahead, waiting for him to go on, luring him with their apparent safety, waiting for him to reach the one rotten rung that would do him in. Some day he would reach it, and it would crack under him, or his fingers would slip and hurtle him into the abyss under his charred engine.

Offensive patrols and escort for the artillery observation squadron filled their time, with sometimes a road strafe to vary the monotony. These he liked best, for some quaint reason — perhaps because there was less space to fall through. Sometimes there would be a battalion on those roads — a battalion to scatter and knock down like tin soldiers on a nursery floor. Quite impersonal. They were never men to Paterson. Like dolls they ran and like dolls they sprawled awkwardly where they fell.

P.-B. and Trent and Hoyt carried him through somehow. Mallory was back again, but Mallory never counted much with him. P.-B. and Trent and Hoyt were a bulwark. They meant safety. It was good to wake up at night and hear P.-B. snoring on the other cot, to know that Hoyt and Trent were asleep in the next cubicle. It was good to see them stamping to keep warm before the patrol took off in the half light of early morning. So different from one another and yet so alike underneath. Hoyt was nearer his kind than the two others. Tall and spindly like his brother, with a straight, thin nose that quivered slightly at the nostril when he was annoyed. Hoyt, who smiled and sanctioned the childishness of little P.-B., but never quite met it with his own, although always seeming to, on the night trips to Amiens. Trent, glowering and quiet, with a keen hatred for everything political that he learned in the offices of the London and South-Western before the war, when the Army to him had meant young wastrels swanking the Guards' livery in the boxes of theaters — wastrels who had died on the Charleroi Road three years before.

Suddenly, from one of his mother's letters, he found that he had been in France almost three months. He stiffened with the thought and remembered what Hoyt had told him that day he had come: "I've been here three months. When I came, I came just as you did today — pucka green." He knew then that all his hopes were false. He was the same today as he had been that first day. He would always be the same. The spot of fear would always be with him. Some day it would swell and choke him and his hands would function without his frozen brain. He should never have tried to fly. He should have gone into the infantry as his brother had. Too much imagination — too little something. In three months he had learned the ropes, that was all; how to fire and when to fire, where the Archie batteries were near Cambrai, how to ride a cloud and crawl into it — nothing more.

The weeks went on, creeping closer and closer

to the twenty-first of March — the twenty-first of
March — and with them the feeling crept into Paterson's heart — a feeling that something frightful
was to happen. Things had been quiet so long and
casualties had been few. C Flight hadn't been
touched in weeks. He brooded over the thought and
slept badly. He went to Amiens with P.-B. more
frequently. If it was to be any of the three, he knew
he wouldn't be able to stand it. His bulwark would
crumble and break and he would break with it. On
the dawn patrols, those few minutes before they
climbed into the cockpits and took off were agony:
"This will be the day. It must be today. We can't
go on this way. Our luck will break."

One day when they were escorting 119, four dots
dived on them from behind and he knew suddenly
what he would do. Stark, logically, the thing stood
before him and beckoned through the wires of his
center section. If a shot hit his plane, he would go
down. They were far over the lines, taking 110 on
a bombing show. He would wabble down slowly,
pushing his joy-stick from side to side in a slow ellipse as if he were out of control. Then he would
land and run his nose into the ground and be taken
prisoner. The others would see him and swear that
he'd been hit — and he wouldn't do it until his
machine had been hit. That for his own conscience's

sake and for the years he would have to live after-wards.

But A Flight, behind and far above, saw the dots and scattered them, and the chance was gone.

Then day by day he waited for another. He knew that he would do it at the first opportunity. He slept better with the thought, and the minutes seemed shorter now while he waited at dawn for his bus to be run out. All the details were worked out in his mind. If any one of the three were close to him, he'd throw up his hands wildly before he started down. They'd see that and report it. Then when he landed he'd pull out the flare quick and burn his machine so that they would think he had crashed and caught fire. It was so easy!

He spent less time with P.-B. now. Somehow the old freedom was gone. Somehow Hoyt wasn't the same to him either. He was working with three strangers he had never really known — three casual strangers he would leave shortly and never see again.

On the morning of the fourteenth of March the caller turned C Flight out suddenly, without warn-ing, about an hour after P.-B. and Trent had re-turned from Amiens. A special signal had come in from wing headquarters. B Flight had the regular morning patrol, but there was to be an additional offensive patrol besides. A Flight had morning escort and the dusk patrol. That meant C for the special. Paterson could hear Hoyt swearing about it next door. P.-B., across the room, uttered a mighty curse and rolled over. Paterson got him a bucket of cold water and doused his head in it. Trent and Hoyt were still cursing pettishly in the next cubicle.

Sleep-stupid, the four of them stumbled into the mess for hard-boiled eggs and coffee. Mallory and the new man, Crowe, were already eating, white-faced and unshaven. They slumped down beside them in silence.

In silence, they trooped across the dark aero-drome, buttoning their coats and fastening helmet straps against the cold wretchedness of the March wind. The machines were waiting for them in a ghostly line like staring wasps that had eaten the food of the gods and grown to gigantic size.

They climbed in and taxied out mechanically. B Flight had already left on the regular dawn patrol. They blipped their motors and roared away, leaving their echo and the sharp smell of castor oil behind on the empty 'drome.

Hoyt led them south to the crumpled ruins of Péronne and out to the line, climbing high to get the warmth of the sunlight that began to tint the clouds above them. They were going over to Le Cateau and beyond. Intelligence wanted pictures to confirm certain reports of new Hun shell dumps and battery concentration. The photographic planes were to go out and get them under escort as soon as there was enough light. As additional precaution, offensive patrols were to be kept up far over the enemy's lines to insure the success of the pictures. They passed the sullen black stain that was Le Câtelet and turned to the eastward. The ground was already light and the camera busses would be starting.

Hoyt took the roof at eighteen thousand feet and skirted the cloud wisps, watching below for customers. Paterson watched P.-B. anxiously. Then he closed in a trifle and climbed above him, but P.-B. waved him down and wiggled his fingers from the end of his nose.

He looked ahead and down at Trent, who was above and slightly behind Hoyt. Then, suddenly, beyond Trent and far below, he saw a Hun two-seater alone. The old stunt. Hoyt shifted and pulled up his nose to climb above it and wait. Trent followed him up. Somewhere above that two-seater, and a half-mile behind, there would be a flight of Hun scouts skulking under the clouds, waiting to pounce on whoever dived for the two-seater. Hoyt knew it for a decoy. Paterson knew it. They would climb above the cloud edge, circle back, and catch the Hun scouts as they passed underneath.

Paterson trembled slightly. This was his chance
at last. There'd be a long dive and a sure fight from
behind, and in the mix-up he'd wabble down and
out of the war via Lazaret VI in Cologne. He glanced
around to see if Mallory was above him, and suddenly, out of the corner of his eye, he saw P.-B.
shove his nose full down and throw himself into a
straight dive for the decoy bus.

He gazed and shouted "No!" into the roar of his
engine. P.-B., in a hasty temper and half fuddled,
didn't smell the trick. There was one awful second
while Crowe closed up into P.-B.'s place and Hoyt
banked to wait above for the Hun scouts to pounce
on the Camel.

P.-B. fired, pulled up, and dived again, far below
them. The Hun two-seater banked sharply and
came up and over in an Immelmann turn to get
away. P.-B. caught it halfway over and a trickle of
smoke swept out from its engine. Then in an instant
Hoyt dived, with the rest of C Flight after him.

The next thing Paterson knew there were two
Huns on his tail and a stream of tracer bullets
pecking at his left wing. He pulled back on his stick
and zoomed headlong up under Mallory. So close
he was for a second that he could see the wheels
turning slowly on Mallory's undercarriage and al-

most count the spokes glinting in the sunlight where the inside canvas sheathing had been taken off.

Mallory pulled away from him in a quick climbing turn and the Huns passed underneath, banking right and left. Paterson picked the left-hand one, thundered down on him in a short dive, and let go a burst of ten shots into the pilot's back. He saw the pilot's head snap sideways and his gloved hands fly up from the controls. Then Mallory dived over him after the other one. He turned in a wild split-air and followed Mallory.

There were more Huns below him and to the left, with two of the C Flight Camels diving and bucking between them. He raced furiously into a long dive, picked the nearest, and opened fire again in short, hammering bursts. His Hun wabbled and started down awkwardly in long sweeps. He picked another, still farther below, and pushed his stick forward until the rush of air gagged him. Wildly he fired as he ploughed down on it, and the chatter of his guns stabbed through the roar of his engine. He yelled like a madman, shot under the Hun, pulled up sharply, and fired into its gray mud-streaked belly. There was a fan of scarlet flame and a shock that tossed him to one side. He stalled and whipped out into a spin. Far below him he could see the decoy two-seater trailing a long plume of reddish smoke and flopping, wings over, toward the floor.

Then, suddenly, he saw his chance to wabble down and get away. He ruddered out of the spin and ran his stick once through the slow ellipse he had planned. But somehow he had to force himself to do it. There wasn't the relief he had expected. He looked back. Three C Flight machines were still above him, fighting madly — P.-B., Trent, and Hoyt. No — not this time. He pulled his stick back and climbed up. There were five Huns circling the Camels. It was a long shot, but he fired at the nearest and came up under the tail just as one of the Camels hurtled into a nose dive, twisted over, and snapped off both wings. He saw the pilot's arms raised wildly in the cockpit and no more.

Blood streamed into his mouth. He had torn his lips with his teeth in the excitement. The warm salty tang mounted to his brain. His goggles were sweat-fogged. His fingers ached with their pressure on the joy-stick, and his arm was numb to the elbow. In a spasm of blind hatred, he fired. Tracers raced across his top plane and struck with little smoke puffs that ripped the fabric into ribbons. His own bullets clawed at the Hun above him and fanged home.

He threw himself up and over in an Immelmann turn and came under the next, still firing. He let go his stick and jerked his Lewis gun down its sliding mount on his top plane. It fired twice and jammed. He yanked madly at the cocking lug, but it stuck halfway. He hurtled down again in another spin. The ground swept around in a quick arc that ended in clouds and more Hun busses. He caught his thrashing joy-stick. Again the ground flashed through his center section struts in a brown smudge, with the blaze of the sun hanging to one end of it. Then there was a Camel above him and a Camel below him. He closed in on the one below and squinted at the markings. Hoyt. He looked up at the other Camel, but the numerals on the side of its fuselage were hidden with a torn flap of fabric. Together, the three turned westward and started back.

Presently, near the line, the bus above him wabbled and dipped its nose. He stared at it. It went into a long, even glide that grew slowly steeper as he watched. He looked down for Huns. There were none. The glide became a dive, the dive twisted into an aimless spin, like the flopping of a lazy swimmer turning over in shallow water. The spin flattened and the Camel whipped out upside down, stalled, snapped out again, and again spun downward in that ghastly slow way. Over and over, only to whip out, stall and spin again. It was miles below him now. Nothing to do. Fascinated, he watched it as he followed Hoyt's tail. It was a mere dot now, flashing once or twice in the sun as it flopped over and over. Close to the ground now — closer. Then, suddenly, a tiny sheet of pink flame leaped up like the flash of a far beacon. That was all.

Hoyt was side-slipping below him, and he saw his own aerodrome under the leading edge of his bottom wing. He followed Hoyt down. They landed together and taxied slowly in toward the hangars. They stopped side by side and climbed out stiff-legged. Paterson looked down and saw that his right flying boot was torn and flayed into shreds across the outer side. There was a jagged fringe on the skirt of his coat where the leather had been ripped into ruffles. Dumbly, he looked back into his cockpit. The floor boards were splintered and the wicker arm of his seat was eaten away. He shrugged and walked over toward Hoyt. There was blood on the rabbit fur of Hoyt's goggles, blood that oozed slowly down and dripped from his chin piece in bright drops.

They walked into the flight office and slumped into chairs. Hoyt ripped off his helmet and dabbed at the scratch on his cheek. "I'm glad you got out, Pat," he said absently.

Then the fear spot broke and spattered into the four corners of Paterson's soul. He sprang up trembling, with his fists beating the air.

"The dirty lice!" he screamed. "They've killed P.-B.! They've killed Trent! D'y hear me, Hoyt?— they've killed 'em! They're gone! They'll never come back! They've —"

Hoyt's voice came evenly, calmly, through his screaming. "Steady, boy! Steady! You can't help it. No one can. Steady, now!"

A mat of white oil-splotched faces stared at them from the open doorway that led into the hangar. The boy turned wildly. "Clear out!" he shrieked. They vanished, open-mouthed. Hoyt drew him down into a chair. "No, Hoyt, no! Can't you see? P.-B. and you and Trent have meant everything to me. I can't go on. I've fought this thing till I'm crazy." Hoyt reached quickly and slammed the door. "I've fought it night and day!" He threw up his arms hopelessly and covered his face with his shaking hands.

Hoyt put his hand on his trembling shoulders and patted them. "Steady, now! Steady! None of that!" he said awkwardly.

Paterson's head whipped down across his sprawled

arms on the desk top and the sobs tore at his throat in great gusts that choked him. "Oh, God!" he sobbed. "What's it all about, Hoyt? What's the use of it?"

"Steady, son! I don't know. Nobody knows. It just happened, as everything happens. It's much too late to talk causes. We're here and we know what we have to do. That's enough for us. It's all we have, anyway, so it must be enough."

Someone knocked at the door. "Come in." It was the runner from squadron office. He saluted. "Yes?" said Hoyt.

The man glanced at Paterson's face and snapped his eyes quickly back to the captain's.

"Beg pardon, sir," he said. "Squadron's just been signaled through wing. One of the C Flight machines came down near B Battery, the 212th."

"Who was it?" asked Hoyt.

"Lieutenant Mallard, they reported it, sir. That'll be Lieutenant Mallory, won't it?"

"Yes." Hoyt's voice was quite flat. "Thank you."

The man saluted again and shut the door. Paterson stood up suddenly and grabbed Hoyt's arm. "Listen, skipper!" Hoyt's eyes met his calmly. "I'm going to tell you something. I'll feel better if I do. I've been a weak sister in this flight. I've planned for days to go down and let myself be

taken prisoner — to get out of it all. I've been sick
of it — sick of it, d'y' hear, until I couldn't think
straight. I wanted to get out alive. I wanted to get
away in any way I could. This morning I broke.
I let go and started down —"

Hoyt smiled. "Your trouble, Pat, is that you
think you're the only person in this jolly old war."

Paterson stared at him. "But I did! I started
down, out of it, this morning!"

"How'd you get here?" asked Hoyt.

"But if I hadn't broken for that moment this
morning —"

"That's a lie!" snapped Hoyt. "You're talking
poobah! I know how those things happen. If P.-B.
hadn't gone down after the two-seater they'd all
be here now; and by the same reasoning, if my
aunt wore trousers she'd be my uncle. The important thing is that it's you and me now and
nothing else matters. We'll have four brand-new
men to whip into shape tomorrow, and whatever
you think of yourself, you've got to do it. I can't
do much, for I'll be ahead, leading. You'll be behind them and you'll have to do it all. They'll be
frightened and nervous and green, but the job's
to be done. Understand? You got to goad them on
and get them out of trouble and watch them every
minute, so that in time they'll be as good as P.-B.

and Trent — so that when their turn comes they can do for other green men what P.-B. and Trent did for you. Do you see now what this morning has done for you?" He paused for a moment, and then, in a lower tone: "Afraid? Who isn't afraid? But it doesn't do any good to brood over it."

C Flight did no duty the next day, nor the day following. Hoyt went up to the 212th and identified Mallory for burial, while Paterson flew back to the Pool for the replacement pilots and a new Camel for Hoyt.

In Amiens he heard the first whispered rumors of what was going to happen. Intelligence was ranting for information. Everybody had the story and nobody was right. The hospitals were evacuating as fast as possible. Fresh battalions were being hustled up. It wasn't a push. Anyone could tell that with half an eye. Something the Hun was doing. The spring offensive a month earlier this year. G.H.Q. was plugging the gaps frantically, replacing and reinforcing and wondering where the hammer would fall and what it would carry with it. Hence the pictures that had cost the lives of P.-B. and Trent. The air itself trembled with uncertainty, and rumors flew fast and thick.

Paterson flew back with the four new pilots and

brought the rumors with him. Hoyt had more to barter in exchange. The talk ran riot at dinner.

"It's a Hun push, all right, but where, nobody knows. We'll have word in a day or so, but it'll be wrong whatever it is, mark what I say!"

And then on the evening of the twentieth things started. A signal came for the major just as they sat down to mess. He went out and presently called out the three flight commanders. When they came back they took their places thoughtfully. Silence trembled in the room like the hush that precedes the first blasting stroke of a great bell in a cathedral tower. The major swept his eyes down the board.

"You will remain at the aerodrome tonight, gentlemen. Luggage is to be packed and placed on lorries which Mr. Harbord is providing for that purpose." He paused for a moment. "This is a precautionary move, gentlemen. We are to be ready to retire at a moment's notice. Flight commanders have the map squares of the new aerodrome. You can take that up later among yourselves." He leaned back in his chair and beckoned to the mess sergeant. "Take every officer's order, sergeant, and bring me the chit."

The talk broke in a wild flood that roared and crackled down the length of the table. The tin walls trembled with the surge of it and the echoes broke in hot discord among the rough pine rafters. Offensive patrols for all three flights, to start at five minutes to 4 A.M. Air domination must be maintained. Wing's instructions were to stop everything at all costs. Go out and fight and shut up. Somebody presented the adjutant with the sugar bowl and asked him if he had his umbrella for the trip back. The adjutant had spent eighteen days without soles to his boots in 1914.

About ten o'clock, Hoyt called the five men of C Flight into his hut. "Tomorrow, something is going to happen, I'm afraid, and you've got to meet it without much experience. What I want you to understand is simply this: You've got Pat and you've got me. Follow us and do what we do. We won't let you down so far as it is humanly possible. If the flight gets split up in a dog fight, then fight your way out two and two — and go back to the new 'drome two and two. Don't go separately. Further" — he paused — "if anything happens to me" — Paterson looked up at him quickly and something tugged sharply at his heart; Hoyt went on quietly — "take your lead from Mr. Paterson. You'll be Number 5, Darlington. You'll climb up as deputy leader. And if anything happens to Pat, then it's up to you to bring the rest home." He smiled. "Oh yes, one more thing: The fact that we're moving back to a new aerodrome seems to indicate that staff thinks nothing can stop the Hun from breaking through. The fact that nothing can stop the Hun seems to indicate that, for the nonce, we are losing our part of the war. If the thought will help you — it's yours without cost."

The caller rapped sharply and threw back the door. Paterson leaped to his feet half asleep and pushed back the window curtains. The clouds were down to about four hundred feet, lowering in a gray mass over the mist on the aerodrome. He went into the next cubicle and turned Hoyt out. Hoyt sat up on the cot edge and ran his hand across his forehead.

"Stop the caller," he said. "Let's see what's what before we turn everybody out." They shrugged into their flying coats and groped down the passage to the major's cubicle in the next hut block.

"Let 'em sleep," said the major. "Can't do anything in this muck. Turn out one officer in each flight to watch for the break and to warn the rest. Send Harbord to me if you see him wandering about."

They woke up the skippers of A and B Flights and told them the news. Paterson took the watch for C. He turned up his coat collar and went out. It was cold and miserable in the open, and the chill crept into his bones.

Presently to the eastward there came a low roar. He looked at his wristwatch. The hands pointed to six minutes to four o'clock. The ground trembled slightly to the sound of the distant guns and the air stirred in faint gusts. The push had started. His muscles stiffened at the knees as he listened. The first shock of the guns was raw and sharp in the quiet air; then it settled into a lower, full-throated rumble like the heavy notes of an organ growling in an underground basilica. Now it rose again in its greater volume — rose steadily, slowly, as if it were a colossal express train hammering down the switch points at unthinkable speed. Presently it soared to its highest pitch and held the blasting monotony of its tone. The minutes ticked off, but the guns never faltered in their symphony of blood. At 4:35 one pipe of the organ to the southeastward cut out suddenly and almost immediately began again, closer than before. Again it broke as he listened, and crept nearer still.

He walked down the line of huts, thrashing his arms and blowing on his cold hands. An impersonal thing to him, yet he shivered slightly and stared upward at the low clouds. Men out there to the eastward were in it. The suspense was over for them. And suddenly he found himself annoyed at the delay, annoyed at the fog and clouds above, that kept him on the ground. He wanted to see what was going on — to know. He turned impatiently and went into the mess. The sergeant brought him coffee, and presently Muirhead of A Flight came in with Church of B.

"It's on," Church said absently. "I suppose this fog means action up the line."

They drank their coffee while the sound of the guns crept nearer and nearer, and one by one the rest of the squadron drifted in for breakfast.

Hoyt sat down next to Paterson. "I don't like it," he said. "Something is giving way up there." He went to the window and looked out. "Clouds are higher," he said, "and the fog's lifted a bit. What do you think, Major?"

They crowded out of the mess doorway and stood in an anxious knot, staring upward. It was well after six o'clock.

"All right" — the major turned around — "get ready to stand by."

C Flight collected in a little knot in front of Hoyt's Camel. Paterson kept his eyes on Hoyt and stamped his feet to get the circulation up. A strange elation crept into his veins and warmed him. In a moment now — in a moment. Awkward waiting

here. Awkward standing around listening to Darlington curse softly and pound his hands together.

Somewhere behind him on the road, a motorbike
roared through the mist, and then to the southward
a shell crashed not a thousand yards from the
'drome, and the echo of it thumped off across the
fields. Darlington jumped and stared at the mush-
room of greasy black smoke. A moment more — a
moment now. Paterson reached over and tapped
Darlington's sleeve. "Keep your guns warm, old
boy." Darlington nodded fiercely.

The major climbed into his cockpit and a mechanic leaped to the propeller. The engine coughed
once and the propeller snapped back. The mechanic
leaped at it again. It spun down and melted into
a circle of pale light. Everyone was climbing in.
Hoyt put a leg up into his stirrup.

They were taxiing out into the open ground,
with the mechanics running after them. Presently
they could see the road. Paterson stared at it in
amazement. It was brown and crawling with lorries
and troops. Something had happened! A Flight,
with the major, sang off across the ground and
took the air together in a climbing turn. B Flight
waited a brief second and followed. Out of the
corner of his eye Paterson could see the mess sergeant climbing up on the lorry seat beside Har-

bord, the equipment officer. Then Hoyt waved his hand. Mechanics yanked at the chock ropes and waved them off. They blipped their motors and raced out after Hoyt.

At five hundred feet they took the roof in the lacy fringe of the low clouds. Bad, very bad, Paterson thought. He ran his thumb across the glass face of his altimeter and his glove became wet with the beaded moisture. He could hardly see Darlington's tail. Ahead of them the clouds were a trifle higher. Hoyt led them up and turned northward. Murder to cross the line at that height, with the barrage on. Darlington was lagging a bit. Afraid of the clouds. He dived on Darlington's tail and closed him up on Number 3. Darlington glanced back at him and ducked his head.

Hoyt was circling back now in a broad sweep. Over there somewhere was Cambrai. He looked up for an instant just in time to see the underside of a huge plane sweep over him. He ducked at the sight of the black crosses, but the plane was gone before he could whip his Lewis gun into action. Almost immediately one corner of his windshield ripped away and the triplex glass blurred with a quick frosting of a thousand cracks. He cursed into the roar of his motor and kept on.

They were higher now, but the visibility was

frightful — like flying in a glass ball that had been streaked with thick, dripping soapsuds. Here a glimpse and a rift that closed up as soon as you looked; there a blank wall, tapering into tantalizing shreds that you couldn't quite see beyond. He fidgeted in his cockpit and turned his head from Hoyt, below him, to the gray emptiness behind. Nothing.

Presently Hoyt banked around, and following him, the compass needle on Paterson's instrument board turned through a half circle. They were going back toward the south again and climbing still higher. An even thousand feet now — just under the rising, ragged clouds. He felt a drop of rain strike his cheek where his chin piece ended. It bit his skin like a thorn and stung for seconds afterward. His goggles were fogging. He ran a finger up under them and swept the lenses.

Then, in a breath, it happened. A gray flash swept down out of the clouds in front of the formation. Hoyt zoomed to avoid it. The Hun zoomed, and they came together and melted into each other in a welter of torn, rumpled wings and flying splinters. Something black and kicking rose out and disappeared. The cords stood out in Paterson's neck and his throat closed. Somewhere his stomach leaped and kicked inside of him, trying to get out, and he saw coffee dripping from the dials of his instruments.

In a second he had thrown his stick forward and gone down into Hoyt's place. He didn't dare look — he couldn't look. He was screaming curses at the top of his voice and the screams caught in his throat in great sobs. His goggles were hopelessly fogged. He ripped them off. Behind him the four new men closed in tightly, with Darlington above them as deputy leader.

There was blood again on his lips. He pulled back his stick and climbed. There, somewhere in the clouds, were the men who had done it! All right! All right! His eyes stung and wept with the force of the wind, and his cheeks quivered under the lash of the raindrops. With his free hand, fist clenched, he pounded his knee in stunned anguish until his muscles ached. Hoyt! Hoyt! Then he saw what he wanted, and dived down furiously at the shape in the mist. Bullets tore at his top plane and raked across the cowling behind him. He closed on the Hun and sent it spinning. There was another — three — five — nothing but Huns. He dived in between them. Fine! He was screaming again and firing. He forgot he was flying. The joy-stick thrashed crazily between his knees, and the ground and the clouds were a muddy gray scarf that swept

from side to side across his eyes. Guns were the
thing. Once, in a quick flash, he saw tiny men running upside down through the ring sight of his
Lewis gun — the gun on his top plane — funny.

His wrists ached and his fingers were quite dead
against the Bowden trigger. No, not that; that's a
Camel — Darlington. He grabbed at his joy-stick
and pulled it back. Funny how hard it was to pull
it. Another Camel swept in beside him, and another, with startling suddenness. It had been a long
time now — a long time. Somebody had been afraid
once and there had been a man named Hoyt. No,
Hoyt was dead. Hoyt had been killed days before.
Must have been P.-B. P.-B was probably in Amiens
by now. He'd left in the tender at six o'clock. And
always his guns chattered above the roar of his
engine.

Abruptly, the cross wires of his center section
raced up to him from a great distance and stopped
just before his eyes. He wondered where they had
been all this time. He stared past them into the
light disc of his propeller, and again the rain lashed
into his face and stung him. He caught at the kicking joy-stick and held on to it with both hands — but
one hand fell away from it and wouldn't come back.
With an effort he pulled back his stick to climb
up under the clouds again. Must be up under the

clouds. Must wait and get more Huns. Funny things, Huns. Clumsy, stupid gray things you shot at and sent down. Go home soon, rest a bit, and get some more. He laughed softly to himself. Joke. Funniest thing in the world.

The center section wires clouded up before his eyes and started to race away from him. Here! That's bad! Can't fly without center section wires. He chuckled a bit over that. Absurd to think of flying without center section wires! Come back here! You come back!

Just as his eyes closed, he saw a streak of roadway flicker through the struts of his left wing. There were faces on it quite close to him — faces that were white and staring; faces with arms raised above them. Funny. He whipped back his joy-stick with a convulsive jerk, and then his head crashed forward and he threw up his arm to keep his teeth from being bashed out against the compass.

It was very dark — dark except for a dancing blue light far away. He moved slightly. Something cool touched his forehead.

"All right," he muttered; "that's all right now. You just follow me." Someone whispered. He opened his eyes and stared into the darkness. "No," he said quite plainly. "I mean it! Hoyt's dead. I saw him go down."

He felt something sharp prick his arm. "You've got the new aerodrome pinpointed, haven't you?" he asked.

A soft voice said: "Yes. Sh-h-h!"

"No," he said, "I can't. Darlington's alone now, and I've got to go back. They're green, but they're good boys." He moved his legs to get up.

"No," said the voice beside him.

"Oh, yes," he said quietly. "Really, this is imperative. I know I crashed."

A stealthy languor crept across his chest and flowed down toward his legs. He thought about it for a moment. "I ought to go," he said pettishly. "But I'm so tired."

"Yes," said the voice. "Go to sleep now."

"Right-o," he said. "You call a tender and wake — me — half — an — hour." He was quiet for a moment more and then he chuckled softly. "Tell 'em it's poobah," he said sharply.

"All right," said the voice. "It's poobah."

His breathing became quiet and regular, and footsteps tiptoed softly down the ward away from his bed.

Verdun Belle

by Alexander Woollcott

I first heard the saga of Verdun Belle's adventure
as it was being told one June afternoon under a
drowsy apple tree in the troubled valley of the
Marne.

The story began in a chill, grimy Lorraine village, where, in hovels and haymows, a disconsolate
detachment of United States marines lay waiting for
the order to go up into that maze of trenches of
which the crumbling traces still weave a haunted
web around the citadel bearing the immortal name
of Verdun.

Into this village at dusk one day in the early
spring of 1918 there came out of space a shabby,
lonesome dog — a squat setter of indiscreet, com-
plex, and unguessable ancestry.

One watching her as she trotted intently along
the aromatic village street would have sworn that

she had an important engagement with the mayor and was, regretfully, a little late.

At the end of the street she came to where a young buck private lounged glumly on a doorstep. Halting in her tracks, she sat down to contemplate him. Then, satisfied seemingly by what she sensed and saw, she came over and flopped down beside him in a most companionable manner, settling herself comfortably as if she had come at last to her long journey's end. His pleased hand reached over and played with one silken chocolate-colored ear.

Somehow that gesture sealed a compact between those two. There was thereafter no doubt in either's mind that they belonged to each other for better or for worse, in sickness and in health, through weal and woe, world without end.

She ate when and what he ate. She slept beside him in the hay, her muzzle resting on his leg so that he could not get up in the night and go forgetfully back to America without her noticing it.

To the uninitiated onlookers her enthusiasm may not have been immediately explicable. In the eyes of his top sergeant and his company clerk he may well have seemed an undistinguished warrior, freckle-faced and immensely indifferent to the business of making the world safe for democracy.

Verdun Belle thought him the most charming person in all the world. There was a loose popular notion that she had joined up with the company as mascot and belonged to them all. She affably let them think so, but she had her own ideas on the subject.

When they moved up into the line she went along and was so obviously trench-broken that they guessed she had already served a hitch with some French regiment in that once desperate region. They even built up the not implausible theory that she had come to them lonely from the grave of some little soldier in faded horizon blue.

Certainly she knew trench ways, knew in the narrowest of passages how to keep out from underfoot, and was so well aware of the dangers of the parapet that a plate of chicken bones up there would not have interested her. She even knew what gas was, and after a reminding whiff of it became more than reconciled to the regulation gas mask, which they patiently wrecked for all subsequent human use because an unimaginative War Department had not foreseen the peculiar anatomical specifications of Verdun Belle.

In May, when the outfit was engaged in the exhausting activities which the High Command was pleased to describe as "resting," Belle thought it a convenient time to present an interested but amply forewarned regiment with seven wriggling casuals, some black and white and mottled as a mackerel sky, some splotched with the same brown as her own.

These newcomers complicated the domestic economy of the leathernecks' haymow, but they did not become an acute problem until that memorable night late in the month when breathless word bade these troops be up and away.

The Second Division of the A.E.F. was always being thus picked up by the scruff of the neck and flung across France. This time the enemy had snapped up Soissons and Rheims and were pushing with dreadful ease and speed toward the remembering Marne.

Foch had called upon the Americans to help stem the tide. Ahead of the marines, as they scrambled across the monotonous plain of the Champagne, there lay amid the ripening wheat fields a mean and hilly patch of timber called Belleau Wood. Verdun Belle went along.

The leatherneck had solved the problem of the puppies by drowning four and placing the other three in a basket he had begged from a village woman.

His notion that he could carry the basket would

have come as a shock to whatever functionary back in Washington designed the marine pack, which, with its neat assortment of food supplies, extra clothing, emergency restoratives, and gruesome implements for destruction, had been so painstakingly calculated to exhaust the capacity of the human back. But in his need the young marine somehow contrived to add an item not in the regulations, namely, one basket containing three unweaned and faintly resentful puppies.

By night and by day the troop movement was made, now in little wheezing trains, now in swarming lorries, now afoot.

Sometimes Belle's crony rode. Sometimes (under pressure of popular clamor against the room he was taking up) he would yield up his place to the basket and jog along with his hand on the tailboard, with Belle trotting behind him.

All the soldiers in Christendom seemed to be moving across France to some nameless crossroads over the hill. Obviously this was no mere shift from one quiet sector to another. They were going to war.

Everyone had assured the stubborn youngster that he would not be able to manage, and now misgivings settled on him like crows.

He guessed that Verdun Belle must be wondering

too. He turned to assure her that everything would be all right. She was not there. Ahead of him, behind him, there was no sign of her. No one within call had seen her quit the line. He kept telling himself she would show up. But the day went and the night came without her.

He jettisoned the basket and pouched the pups in his forest-green shirt in the manner of kangaroos. In the morning one of the three was dead. And the problem of transporting the other two was now tangled by the circumstance that he had to feed them.

An immensely interested old woman in the village where they halted at sunup, vastly amused by this spectacle of a soldier trying to carry two nursing puppies to war, volunteered some milk for the cup of his mess kit, and with much jeering advice from all sides, and, by dint of the eye dropper from his pack, he tried sheepishly to be a mother to the two waifs. The attempt was not shiningly successful.

He itched to pitch them over the fence. But if Verdun Belle had not been run over by some thundering camion, if she lived she would find him, and then what would he say when her eyes asked what he had done with the pups?

So, as the order was shouted to fall in, he hitched

his pack to his back and stuffed his charges back into his shirt.

Now, in the morning light, the highway was choked. Down from the lines in agonized, grotesque rout came the stream of French life from the threatened countryside, jumbled fragments of fleeing French regiments. But America was coming up the road.

It was a week in which the world held its breath.

The battle was close at hand now. Field hospitals, jostling in the river of traffic, sought space to pitch their tents. The top sergeant of one such outfit was riding on the driver's seat of an ambulance. Marines in endless number were moving up fast.

It was one of these who, in a moment's halt, fell out of line, leaped to the step of the blockaded ambulance, and looked eagerly into the medico top sergeant's eyes.

"Say, buddy," whispered the youngster, "take care of these for me. I lost their mother in the jam."

The top found his hands closing on two drowsy pups.

All that day the field-hospital personnel was harried by the task of providing nourishment for the two casuals who had been thus unexpectedly attached to them for rations. Once established in a farmhouse (from which they were promptly shelled out) , the top went over the possible provender and found that the pups were not yet equal to a diet of bread, corn syrup, and corned willy. A stray cow, loosed from her moorings in the great flight, was browsing tentatively in the next field, and two orderlies who had carelessly reminisced of life on their farms back home were detailed to induce her cooperation.

But the bombardment had brought out a certain moody goatishness in this cow, and she would not let them come near her. After a hot and maddening chase that lasted two hours, the two milkmen reported a complete failure to their disgusted chief.

The problem was still unsolved at sundown, and the pups lay faint in their bed of absorbent cotton out in the garden, when, bringing up the rear of a detachment of marines that straggled past, there trotted a brown-and-white setter.

"It would be swell if she had milk in her," the top sergeant said reflectively, wondering how he could salvage the mascot of an outfit on the march.

But his larcenous thoughts were waste. At the gate she halted dead in her tracks, flung her head high to sniff the air, wheeled sharp to the left and became just a streak of brown and white against the ground. The entire staff came out and formed a jostling circle to watch the family reunion.

After that it was tacitly assumed that these casuals belonged. When the hospital was ordered to shift farther back beyond the reach of the whining shells, Verdun Belle and the pups were intrusted to an ambulance driver and went along in style. They all moved — bag, baggage, and livestock — into the deserted little Château of the Guardian Angel, of which the front windows were curtained against the eyes and dust of the road, but of which the rear windows looked out across drooping fruit trees upon a sleepy, murmurous, multicolored valley, fair as the Garden of the Lord.

The operating tables, with acetylene torches to light them, were set up in what had been a tool shed. Cots were strewn in the orchard alongside. Thereafter for a month there was never rest in that hospital.

The surgeons and orderlies spelled each other at times, snatching morsels of sleep and returning a few hours later to relieve the others. But Verdun Belle took no time off. Between cat naps in the corner, due attentions to her restive brood, and an occasional snack for herself, she managed somehow to be on hand for every ambulance, cursorily examining each casualty as he was lifted to the ground.

Then, in the four o'clock dark of one morning, the orderly bending over a stretcher that had just been rested on the ground was hit by something that half bowled him over.

The projectile was Verdun Belle. Every quivering inch of her proclaimed to all concerned that here was a case she was personally in charge of. From nose to tail tip she was taut with excitement, and a kind of eager whimpering bubbled up out of her as if she ached to sit back on her haunches and roar to the star-spangled sky but was really too busy at the moment to indulge herself in any release so satisfying to her soul. For here was this mess of a leatherneck of hers to be washed up first. So like him to get all dirty the moment her back was turned! The first thing he knew as he came to was the feel of a rough pink tongue cleaning his ears.

I saw them all next day. An ambling passer-by, I came upon two cots shoved together under an apple tree. Belle and her ravenous pups occupied one of these. On the other the young marine — a gas case, I think, but maybe his stupor was shell shock and perhaps he had merely had a crack on the head — was deep in a dreamless sleep. Before drifting off he had taken the comforting precaution to reach out one hand and close it tight on a silken ear.

Later that day he told me all about his dog. I doubt if I ever knew his name, but some quirk of memory makes me think his home was in West Philadelphia and that he had joined up with the marines when he came out of school.

I went my way before dark and never saw them again, nor ever heard tell what became of the boy and his dog. I never knew when, if ever, he was shipped back into the fight, nor where, if ever, those two met again. It is, you see, a story without an end, though there must be those here and there in this country who witnessed and could set down for us the chapter that has never been written.

I hope there was something prophetic in the closing paragraph of the anonymous account of Verdun Belle which appeared the next week in the A.E.F. newspaper, *The Stars and Stripes*. That paragraph was a benison which ran in this wise:

Before long they would have to ship him on to the evacuation hospital, on from there to the base hospital, on and on and on. It was not very clear to anyone how another separation could be prevented. It was a perplexing question, but they knew in their hearts they could safely leave the answer to someone else. They could leave it to Verdun Belle.

IN THE
SECOND
WORLD WAR

1939-1945

From
Commander-in-Chief
Franklin Delano Roosevelt

On January 6, 1941, President Franklin Delano Roosevelt told Congress:

"In the future days, which we seek to make secure, we look forward to a world founded upon four essential human freedoms. The first is freedom of speech and expression — everywhere in the world. The second is freedom of every person to worship God in his own way — everywhere in the world. The third is freedom from want — which, translated into world terms, means economic understandings which will secure to every nation a healthy peaceful life for its inhabitants — everywhere in the world.

The last is freedom from fear — which, translated into world terms, means a worldwide reduction of armaments to such a point and in such a thorough fashion that no nation will be in a position to commit an act of physical aggression against any neighbor — anywhere in the world."

From

Supreme Commander of the Allied Expeditionary Force for the Invasion of Europe, Dwight D. Eisenhower

On D-Day, June 6, 1944, Supreme Commander Dwight D. Eisenhower said in his Order of the Day:

"Soldiers, sailors and airmen of the Allied Expeditionary Force: You are about to embark upon a great crusade toward which we have striven these many months. The eyes of the world are upon you. The hopes and prayers of liberty-loving peoples everywhere march with you."

Reluctant Hero

by William Chamberlain

"Speaking of riddles," Hobey Dunn said, "I ran into a dilly during the fighting in the Philippines. It concerned a soldier named Minor — at least that was the name the Army knew him by then."

"Not his real name?" I asked.

"Nope," Hobey said. "Back during the Civil War, so I've read, a drafted man could hire a substitute to take his place in the Army. Well, Tom Minor pulled a switch on that."

"So?" I said. "What kind of switch?"

"Tom didn't hire a civilian to take his place as a soldier," Hobey told me. "He hired a soldier to take his place as a civilian. Lucky for me he did, too. I wouldn't be here if he hadn't."

We had reached Carigara Bay on Leyte (Hobey said) when I first ran into Tom. I was commanding a battalion and this night we went into a perimeter

astride the Capoocan Road. About 0400 the rain began to come down in sheets. It was nice weather for
a banzai attack, and, brother, we got one. It hit
hard into Love, which was the rifle company farthest
forward.

Communications went out, and I got itchy and
started up there. Fool thing to do. In the night and
rain I got lost. I was blundering around like a stupid
cow when an M-1 went off almost under my nose.
Luckily I'd stumbled into one of our positions.

I yelled, "Hold it! This is Dunn!"

"Get down in here, Colonel," a crisp voice said.
"The Nips are liable to chop your head off if you
don't."

I slid into the hole — it was a big one with five
men in it. Two of them were dead Japanese, I
found out. It was too dark to tell much about the
three others except that they were Americans.

"Where's the company C.P.?" I asked when I got
my breath. Things had quieted down except for
sporadic firing off to the left. It still rained. "I'm
looking for Captain McNamara."

"He ought to be back down the road a ways," the
first speaker said. "How's for helping Jake tie his
leg up, Colonel? Wiley, you keep an eye on things.
I'm going to have a look out front."

"You're crazy, kid!" a hoarse voice protested. "Go

out there and you're dead. Them boondocks are crawlin' with Japs!"

"I'll be back," the other said easily.

He checked his Tommy gun and went, the jungle and the rain swallowing him. I didn't know it then, but he was also carrying a Filipino bolo — a wicked razor-edged chopper he'd salvaged from somewhere. I located Jake by his swearing; he was propped up in the bottom of the hole. An enemy grenade had hashed up his knee. We bandaged it the best we could, working by feel in the dark.

"It's too quiet," Wiley said uneasily. "I don't like it. I wish Tom would get back."

Tom was the one who'd left, I guessed. I wondered if maybe Tom had decided that things were no good up here and had taken a powder while he had the chance. I didn't like the idea.

"Who's Tom?" I asked.

"Him?" Jake grunted. "Tom Minor."

"Is he a noncom? In command here?"

"Naw," Wiley said on my right. "He ain't a noncom. He ain't nothing but a dogface like us. Hell, he's just a kid."

I didn't inquire further because that banzai scream was beginning to fill the night again. It's a sound that lifts the hair up along your spine, and it was coming right at us. I thought, *Well this is it.* Jake grunted as he pulled the pin from a grenade; Wiley's BAR began its methodical whump-whump-whump beside me, and I opened up with my carbine. *I'd do about as well throwing rocks,* I decided, as squat figures began to take shape through the rain.

Japanese — you could smell them! Their screams were in our ears, and their bayonets were darned near in our bellies when a wicked burst of Tommy-gun fire ripped in from the flank, and the leading Japanese went down. More of them kept coming. They went down too.

"Tom!" Wiley yelled. "Good boy! Pour it into 'em!"

I didn't have time to be ashamed of what I'd thought about Tom earlier. I did decide that if we got out of this I'd see to it that Tom started wearing chevrons. I hadn't even seen his face, but he looked like a lot of soldier to me. Then I stopped thinking, because my carbine jammed, and a Japanese was coming for me with his bayonet. He'd have skewered me like a pig if Tom Minor hadn't suddenly showed up. He took care of the Jap.

Well, we did get out of it. As the night began to gray, a grimy-faced sergeant brought up a couple of squads to reinforce us. After it got light we

counted thirty-one dead Japanese on the Capoocan
Road. I looked around for Minor, but he was gone
again.

"He's up ahead scoutin' for Japs," Wiley explained to me. "That guy's a regular one-man
army."

I didn't have a chance to do anything about Tom's
promotion right away, because it was right after that
when we went into the fight for Breakneck Ridge.
That was a bad one, and we took it on the chin good.
Finally it was over, and they pulled us back into the
Leyte Valley to rest and refit. I remembered Tom
Minor and sent for Pat McNamara, who was Tom's
company commander.

"Have you a soldier named Minor in the company, Pat?" I asked, almost afraid to hear the answer
for fear I'd find the kid was dead. His kind usually
doesn't last long. "Private Tom Minor?"

"Tom?" Pat said. "Sure I got him, Colonel.
Why?"

I told Pat about that night on the Capoocan
Road. "He's a born leader, Pat," I said. "I don't
mean to interfere with your business, but I think
that man should be a sergeant."

"So do I," Pat grunted. "I've sent his name in a
dozen times. Regiment's turned thumbs down on
it each time."

"For Pete's sake, why?"

"You ought to see his record, sir," Pat said. "It's a real doozy. A dozen A.W.O.L.'s back in the States. Insubordination, losing Government property, gold-bricking, shirking important duty — just about every crime in the book except high treason."

"That's screwy," I said. "I'll have a look for myself."

I got the record from the personnel people. Pat had been right — it was a doozy. I noticed one thing, though. Tom Minor had joined the regiment as a replacement at Hollandia in New Guinea, where we'd staged for the Leyte show. During the time he'd been with us, no new entries had been added to his crime sheet.

I had Tom report to me that afternoon and got my first good look at him. I liked what I saw. His fatigues were scrubbed and his boots were clean. He had the alert, confident air of a man who took pride in himself and in his outfit. The only non-regulation thing about him was the bolo slung at his hip, and that was an item I could darned well afford to overlook, considering everything.

The record in my hand said that Private Thomas P. Minor was twenty-four years old, stood five-feet-eleven, weighed one hundred and sixty pounds and had sandy hair and gray eyes. The age was the only part of the description that didn't fit. I thought as I looked at Tom. There was a certain maturity in his face and a sort of wariness behind his eyes, but I would have bet a month's pay that he hadn't yet seen his twentieth birthday — let alone his twenty-fourth.

Another thing bothered me. I could find nothing in his appearance or manner that bore out that impressive delinquency sheet in his record. Actually I had the feeling that I had known this boy somewhere before, but couldn't put my finger on the where and when.

"Hello, Tom," I said. "Sit down."

He said, "Yes, sir," and sat, looking back at me composedly, though I saw his eyes flick to that record in front of me.

"I've been going over your record," I said. "You managed to get into a good bit of trouble during your first nine months in the Army, it seems. Want to tell me about it?"

He thought that over for a moment. "No, sir," he said then. "I guess the record's true. I did some pretty stupid things back in the States. I think I've sort of settled down now."

I wasn't satisfied, but I knew that was all I was going to get — for the time being, at least. "All right," I said. "We'll forget the record. You've demonstrated that you're a fine combat soldier and that you've got outstanding leadership qualities. I'm going to see to it that you're promoted to sergeant, Tom."

I saw that I'd really got through to him then, because his face lighted up, the boyishness showing through. "Thanks, Colonel," he said. "My fa — I mean, I'd sure be proud of that."

"Also," I went on, "I'm recommending you for the Silver Star for what you did that night on the Capoocan Road, Tom."

I thought that would please him even more, but I was wrong. There was a change in his voice as he said, "Sir, I hope the colonel won't do that. It — well, it'd be a favor to me if he didn't."

"Why not?" I asked. "You earned it, for Pete's sake!"

"I'd just rather the colonel didn't, sir."

I dismissed him and sat there trying to figure that one out, but I had no luck. I thought of how he'd addressed me in the third person when he'd been upset. That was an old-army custom pretty much neglected in the new army we'd put together with the draft. I felt that ought to mean something to me, but it didn't. Finally I decided that the whole thing was screwy and forgot about it.

Tom was promoted to sergeant, and I sent the

Silver Star recommendation in just the same. I heard nothing further on that, but I knew that those things take time. We finished up on Leyte, and the division got a short rest as 1944 ended. Then the island-hopping began — Mindoro, Lubang, Luzon, Corregidor. Early in April the rumor spread that we were going south to Mindanao. I was promoted to bird colonel, going to another regiment, and I lost track of Tom. I'd think of the boy occasionally.

When I finally did run into him again, he'd been promoted to second lieutenant. It had been a battle-field promotion, and you can bet that it tickled me mightily. It had happened at a place called Pangar, during the fight across Mindanao, I learned.

Tom's platoon leader got killed in a nasty little fight for a stream crossing, and Tom took over. He worked a couple of squads through the abacá — that's Manila hemp and pure, unadulterated hell to fight through — and he came down on the Japanese flank. His detachment was outnumbered two or three to one, but it had the advantage of surprise. It had a bigger advantage, and that was Tom Minor.

He took them in hard — savagely hard. He was in the lead swinging that wicked bolo. Tom's platoon had a high esteem for that weapon. When the thing was done some forty-odd Nips had died for the emperor, and the platoon had the stream crossing. It happened that the division commander saw the last part of the fight.

"Who's that baby-faced soldier swinging that chopper?" the general growled — the Old Man was a rough egg.

"Sergeant Minor," somebody said.

"Sergeant hell!" the Old Man snorted. "As of now he's Lieutenant Minor, and the regulations and the War Department can stew in their own corruption if they don't like it!"

Well, we crossed the island from Parang on the Moro Gulf — going by way of the National Highway — and, by Harry, we went at a gallop! We came into Davao on the island's far side, by the back door. I won't bore you with the details of that fight — it was the same old deal we'd known since Hollandia in New Guinea. You dug the Japanese out, one by one, and you killed them, because there was no other way.

I got a bullet through my hip that immobilized me temporarily, so the Old Man attached me to the division staff as a sort of higher-numbered cannoneer. I got the odd jobs that nobody else wanted. That was how I ran into J. Wesley Ormund.

The Old Man called me in. "Hobey," he said, "the high brass in Manila have wished off a VIP on us. His name is Ormund, and he's a hot-shot war correspondent with very important connections. We're to show him every courtesy, it says here. I'm turning him over to you as of when he arrives at the airstrip this afternoon."

I stuck my neck out. "Sir," I asked, "would he be the same Ormund who wrote that Lugan story about the brutal American soldiery?"

"He would," the Old Man growled. "What about it?"

"A friend of mine was crucified because of the half-truths in that story," I said. "I might as well tell you — I'm liable to drown this Ormund in the first deep creek we come to."

"Don't bother me with details," the Old Man said — he hadn't liked that story either. "Ormund's your baby. By the way, you're the one who recommended Minor for the Silver Star, aren't you?"

"Yes, sir," I said.

"The recommendation's been approved. I'll present the medal here this evening. Thought you might want to come."

I was pleased. "I'll be there, sir," I said.

That afternoon I picked J. Wesley Ormund up at the division airstrip, brought him to the C.P. and got him all cozy in a native shack we used for visiting firemen. As a person, he didn't seem to be quite the skunk I'd expected him to be. He was about my own age, slightly built, and he had a sharp intelligent face that went with brown eyes and graying hair.

"What kind of a story are you after, Ormund? Another spectacular like you wrote at Lugan?" I asked him.

Ormund's face didn't change its aloof, faintly sardonic expression. "What about the Lugan story?" he asked.

"It was full of distortions and half-truths," I said, hanging onto my temper. "It ruined the career of a fine officer who was guilty of nothing except doing the things that had to be done."

"The careers of officers don't interest me, Dunn," Ormund told me, his voice indifferent. "When I find a story, I write it. If somebody gets hurt in the process, it's just too bad."

"We may as well understand each other," I replied. "You're in my charge while you're with this outfit, and I'll tell you now that there will be no Lugan stories written here."

"Manila might have some ideas on that," he said.

I didn't have any good answer, so I let it go. However, I took him with me that evening to see Tom Minor get his Silver Star. That was a story I'd be glad to have him write, and I filled him in on the details of what had happened on the Capoocan

Road. If any of the story interested him, he managed not to show it.

The staff was gathered in the map room when we reached the C.P. Tom was standing with Pete Johns, one of the Old Man's aides, and his face had a strained and worried look, I thought. Somebody called, "Attention!" and the Old Man came in. Pete and Tom Minor stepped forward, and Pete began to read the citation.

". . . for conspicuous gallantry in action at Capoocan. . . ."

He finished and opened a flat box and held it out to the general. The Old Man lifted out the decoration — a silver star superimposed on a bronze one and hung from a striped ribbon. I glanced at Tom again and was shocked at the misery I saw in his eyes.

Good Lord, I thought, *he's going to refuse it.*

I was right. The Old Man was turning to him when Tom said, "I'm sorry, sir. I can't accept that decoration."

It was one of the few times I ever saw the Old Man surprised. He's got a temper like a bull walrus, and his neck began getting red so that I expected him to explode. He didn't.

"Why not, Lieutenant?" he asked quietly instead.

"I can't explain, sir," Tom said. He stood ramrod-straight, and he didn't look like a kid now. "But I just can't take the medal."

The Old Man looked at him from beneath his bushy eyebrows for a moment longer. Then he said, "Very well. That's all."

Ormund had lost some of his detached aloofness as I took him back to the guest shack. "A man accepting a medal is no story," he said, clipping his words. "There's a story when a man turns down a medal, Dunn. I want to talk to that lieutenant — now!"

"You can talk to him tomorrow," I said, making my words as blunt as I knew how. "He's got other things on his mind tonight."

I left him and found Tom where I expected he would be — about to shove off up the Dalogan valley to where Love Company was fighting to clean the last of the Japanese off Baker Mountain. The moon had come up as I beckoned Tom to one side.

"Tom," I said, "you'd better tell me about it now."

I thought that he was going to refuse, because his face turned hard for a moment. It eased again, and some of the kid showed through. Suddenly I knew why I thought I'd seen him somewhere before.

"I guess I better had, sir," he said quietly.

It was a mixed-up story. Tom's family had always

been army — Regular Army — and he'd grown up with the certain knowledge that one day he would be army too. It was something that had to be — something made up of the clean notes of "Retreat" rising in the sunset, or the cadenced thud of boots as the lines passed in review, or the sound of "Taps" singing a soldier's lullaby as the barracks lights went out.

He was seventeen when Pearl Harbor came. He couldn't wait to go. His father had understood; finally he had given Tom permission to enlist. Tom's mother had violently disapproved.

"I got along swell at the training center, sir," Tom told me. "But then they transferred me to the artillery and sent me to a Coast-defense fort in Virginia — I might as well have stayed a civilian for all the good I was doing. Cutting grass and stuff like that. I took it as long as I could, and then I guess I sort of blew my top. I beat up a couple of guys and smashed some furniture and threw a chair out of a barracks window. They sent me to the hospital for observation. I was emotionally unstable, the doctors said."

Tom's father was in North Africa by then, and his mother took over. She flew out to where Tom was, got hold of a medico who was an old family friend and, when the smoke cleared away, Tom was out of the Army with a medical discharge and a "psycho" tag hung on him. He didn't blame his mother. She probably hadn't meant it to happen that way, but she'd sure ended any army career for Tom.

He tried desperately to get back in, but the Army would have none of him. The regulations of the Medical Department are as immutable as the laws of the Medes and the Persians. To the Army, Tom was a "psycho," and nothing was going to change it.

"I wrote Dad finally," Tom said. "He had friends in the War Department, and they tried to help me get back in, but it was no good."

I guess the kid was going through pure hell. He'd disgraced his father and let his country down, in his book. He thought of trying to enlist under another name, but knew it wouldn't work. He'd be put through all of the regular processing again and, sooner or later, they'd find out who he really was. Then he'd be out of the Army again; he might even be in jail for fraudulent enlistment.

"I figured there was just one way, sir," Tom said. "That was to find somebody in the Army who wanted to get out. If he and I were to trade places it might work, because that way I wouldn't have to go through that processing at the reception center, you see."

"So you found Tom Minor," I said.

Tom nodded. "I ran into him outside a bar. He was a bum — it stuck out all over him — but I couldn't be too choosy. We were about the same build and all. Also he was at a replacement depot waiting to ship overseas, and that meant none of the noncoms or officers knew him. I gave him fifty bucks and took his uniform and checked in at the depot with his pass that night. Nobody paid any attention to me."

"All replacements are orphans," I said.

"I wrote Mom that I'd signed up with the merchant marines," Tom said. "I told her I was going to sea and didn't know when I'd be back. I'd been through basic, so I didn't have any trouble when I joined the regiment. I figured even my bad record wouldn't hurt me if I soldiered hard. I guess you know the rest, sir."

"Yes," I said, "I know the rest, Tom. You're General Luke January's son, aren't you? I should have seen that before — I used to know your father at Fort Benning."

I saw pride flash into Tom's face — even out in the Pacific we knew of the fighting record that Luke

January had hung up in Italy and Europe. Worry came back into Tom's eyes, however.

"About that newspaper fellow tonight, sir," he said. "He won't find out about me, will he? I sure wouldn't want him to write some sort of a story that might hurt Dad."

"There'll be no story, Tom," I said.

But, after he was gone, I wasn't so sure. Also, I'd forgotten to ask him why he'd refused the medal. The next morning Ormund was in my hair. He demanded that I take him to Baker Mountain where Love Company was fighting. I tried to stall.

"There's no story on the mountain," I said.

"I'll be the judge of that." Ormund's sharp face told me he'd found out that Tom was up there. "Either I go, or I radio Manila that you people refuse to cooperate with the press."

He had me, and he knew it. So I got a jeep, and we headed up the valley. There was a passable track as far as the forward artillery positions; after that we'd go the rest of the way on foot. It was about 1530 when we reached the last firing battery.

"We walk from here," I said. The battery exec came up as we unloaded. "Anything doing on the mountain?" I asked him.

"The boys are pushing," he said. "They've got

as far as the big saddle. Still plenty of Japs in front
of them, though."

We started out. The day was hot and the air mug-
gy — as though you were breathing warm tea. Japanese dead were unburied along the trail, and they
stank of decomposition. Presently we crossed a
stream, the water milky as it rushed out of the hills,
and we rested there. Ormund sat in the water and
splashed the lukewarm stuff over his chest and head.

"I want a promise from you," I said.

"You can ask it," he told me heavily.

I'd been mulling the thing over all the way up
the valley and decided this was my best bet. So I
repeated what Tom had said last night. Even Ormund should be able to see that he must lay off
the boy. My gamble lost, because Ormund's face got
sharper.

"So that's the way it is," I ended. "No story."

"There'll be a story when I get through with it,"
Ormund said. My words had meant nothing. "Luke
January's kid hiding in the Army under a phony
name? You're right there'll be a story!"

I came close to shooting him where he sat. I
shouldn't have taken him any farther, but I did.
Maybe I was hoping that a Japanese sniper would
get him — it had happened before. It was late afternoon when we heard an irregular spatter of firing

ahead and came to Love Company's C.P. Tom
Minor had the third platoon, Pat McNamara told
me. They were working along the ridge toward the
peak of Baker.

"Many Japs still up there?" I asked.

"Enough." Pat shrugged. "Three–four hundred,
maybe."

"If they're treed, they're liable to pull a banzai
on you."

"I wouldn't bet against it," McNamara agreed.

We went on. The ridge was thorny with scrub
and broken by steep outcrops, but presently it began to flatten into a shallow saddle. The third
platoon was there, going into a perimeter for the
night while there was still a little daylight left. Tom,
dirt and sweat streaking his face, was checking in
with McNamara over the radio.

"Metthaus and Oliver bought it this afternoon,"
he was saying. "Four others wounded. Otherwise
we're in fair shape. We'll tie in with the second
platoon for the night, skipper."

He checked out, put the handset down, looked
at me absently and then looked past me to Ormund.
I was about to speak when Ormund took the play
out of my hands.

"Hello, January," he said, pushing past me. "I'm
Ormund," and he named the syndicate he worked

for. "I want to know why you refused that decoration last night — the decoration for Tom Minor."

God knows what could have happened, because I saw murder jump into Tom's eyes. He was fingering the bolo at his hip when a burst of fire came from the far side of the saddle fifty yards away. A man's voice carried hoarsely to where we were.

"Look out! Here they come, Toomey! Get that BAR goin' —it's another lousy banzai!"

Small need for that last. The evening was already hideous with the screams of crazed Japanese. The familiar prickle ran along my spine as I grabbed my carbine and followed Tom, racing through the scrub. Ahead of us the saddle exploded with fire; the Japanese had picked their time well, for the perimeter foxholes were not yet dug. The platoon fought in the open. I knelt to fire. In the fading light, squat men ran at us, mouths open as they screeched.

I thought, *Hell must be like this.*

There's no way to describe a banzai charge. It's as wicked as a Doré picture of the Inferno. It is confusion and shouting and garments dipped in blood. Around me a dozen fights went on, men stabbing and gouging and swinging gun butts. A soldier hammered an enemy's brains out with a rock only an instant before his own head was split by a samurai sword. And through it all I was aware of Tom.

He was where it was thickest, his bolo chopping a red swath as his voice lifted above the howl of the fight. "Cut 'em down! Let's go! Come on, let's go!"

It was a terrible battle cry that rang through the gloom as Tom seemed to stand ten feet tall.

"Ah," Ormund said beside me. He was fighting — fighting well. "I wouldn't have missed this. That kid — my Lord, he's wonderful! Magnificent! What a story! *What* a story!

Then suddenly it was over, and the Japanese were pulling back onto the mountain, our bullets following them. Tom was still on his feet, face bleeding and shirt in rags. *Thank God*, I thought, *he's still O.K.*, but my thanksgiving was too soon. A Japanese rifle cracked sharply from the slope ahead, and Tom stumbled backward and fell.

The platoon, what was left of it, saw that and went crazy. Not yelling crazy as the Japanese had been — killing crazy, tight-lipped, silent and grim. As one man it went onto the mountain; when it returned, it had left nothing alive in its wake. I called for an aid man, and he came, bringing litter bearers with him. Vaguely I knew that Ormund was at my shoulder once more.

"Well, you got your story," I said savagely.

Tom had been shot through the body, but he was still conscious. The aid man straightened up, and I saw relief in his face. "His chances ain't too bad, Colonel," he said to me. "We'll get him back to the aid station. All right, you guys."

Now Ormund dropped on one knee to put a hand on Tom's shoulder. "Get back soon, son," he said, and for a hard-boiled newsman his voice was pretty husky. "People like you can't be spared. Why did you refuse that decoration — will you tell me?"

Pain — not from the bullet — showed in Tom's face. "Minor was a bum, sir," he whispered. "It would have dirtied the decoration — I just couldn't take it in his name."

"I understand," Ormund said very softly. "Sometimes the press has the power to do things that others can't. It will do one thing, I promise you. It will see that Luke January's son has the right to wear his own name from now on — and the medal that goes with it. Keep remembering that, Tom."

Tom's smile came briefly, the boyishness showing through. "Thanks, sir," he said. "Dad and I would sure like that."

We watched the litter bearers go down the ridge. Then Ormund turned back to me. "You were wrong, Dunn," he said soberly. "There *was* a story on the mountain. You will like it when you read it."

Two Soldiers

by *William Faulkner*

Me and Pete would go down to Old Man Killegrew's and listen to his radio. We would wait until after supper, after dark, and we would stand outside Old Man Killegrew's parlor window, and we could hear it because Old Man Killegrew's wife was deaf, and so he run the radio as loud as it would run, and so me and Pete could hear it plain as Old Man Killegrew's wife could, I reckon, even standing outside with the window closed.

And that night I said, "What? Japanese? What's a pearl harbor?" and Pete said, "Hush."

And so we stood there, it was cold, listening to the fellow in the radio talking, only I couldn't make no heads nor tails neither out of it. Then the fellow said that would be all for a while, and me and Pete walked back up the road to home, and Pete told me what it was. Because he was nigh twenty and he had done finished the Consolidated last June

and he knowed a heap: about them Japanese dropping bombs on Pearl Harbor and that Pearl Harbor
was across the water.

"Across what water?" I said. "Across that Government reservoy up at Oxford?"

"Naw," Pete said. "Across the big water. The
Pacific Ocean."

We went home. Maw and Pap was already asleep,
and me and Pete laid in the bed, and I still couldn't
understand where it was, and Pete told me again —
the Pacific Ocean.

"What's the matter with you?" Pete said. "You're
going on nine years old. You been in school now
ever since September. Ain't you learned nothing
yet?"

"I reckon we ain't got as fer as the Pacific Ocean
yet," I said.

We was still sowing the vetch then that ought to
been all finished by the fifteenth of November, because Pap was still behind, just like he had been
ever since me and Pete had knowed him. And we
had firewood to git in, too, but every night me and
Pete would go down to Old Man Killegrew's and
stand outside his parlor window in the cold and
listen to his radio; then we would come back home
and lay in the bed and Pete would tell me what it

was. That is, he would tell me for a while. Then he
wouldn't tell me. It was like he didn't want to talk
about it no more. He would tell me to shut up because he wanted to go to sleep, but he never wanted
to go to sleep.

He would lay there, a heap stiller than if he was
asleep, and it would be something, I could feel it
coming out of him, like he was mad at me even, only
I knowed he wasn't thinking about me, or like he
was worried about something, and it wasn't that
neither, because he never had nothing to worry
about. He never got behind like Pap, let alone
stayed behind. Pap give him ten acres when he
graduated from the Consolidated, and me and Pete
both reckoned Pap was durn glad to get shut of at
least ten acres, less to have to worry with himself;
and Pete had them ten acres all sowed to vetch and
busted out and bedded for the winter, and so it
wasn't that. But it was something. And still we
would go down to Old Man Killegrew's every night
and listen to his radio, and they was at it in the
Philippines now, but General MacArthur was holding 'um. Then we would come back home and lay
in the bed, and Pete wouldn't tell me nothing or
talk at all. He would just lay there still as a ambush
and when I would touch him, his side or his leg

would feel hard and still as iron, until after a while I would go to sleep.

Then one night — it was the first time he had said nothing to me except to jump on me about not chopping enough wood at the wood tree where we was cutting — he said, "I got to go."

"Go where?" I said.

"To that war," Pete said.

"Before we even finish gittin' in the firewood?"

"Firewood, hell," Pete said.

"All right," I said. "When we going to start?"

But he wasn't even listening. He laid there, hard and still as iron in the dark. "I got to go," he said. "I jest ain't going to put up with no folks treating the Unity States that way."

"Yes," I said. "Firewood or no firewood, I reckon we got to go."

This time he heard me. He laid still again, but it was a different kind of still.

"You?" he said. "To a war?"

"You'll whup the big uns and I'll whup the little uns," I said.

Then he told me I couldn't go. At first I thought he just never wanted me tagging after him, like he wouldn't leave me go with him when he went sparking them girls of Tull's. Then he told me the Army wouldn't leave me go because I was too little, and then I knowed he really meant it and that I couldn't go nohow noways. And somehow I hadn't believed until then that he was going himself, but now I knowed he was and that he wasn't going to leave me go with him a-tall.

"I'll chop the wood and tote the water for you-all then!" I said. "You got to have wood and water!"

Anyway, he was listening to me now. He wasn't like iron now.

He turned onto his side and put his hand on my chest because it was me that was laying straight and hard on my back now.

"No," he said. "You got to stay here and help Pap."

"Help him what?" I said. "He ain't never caught up nohow. He can't get no further behind. He can sho'ly take care of this little shirttail of a farm while me and you are whupping them Japanese. I got to go too. If you got to go, then so have I."

"No," Pete said. "Hush now. Hush." And he meant it, and I knowed he did. Only I made sho' from his own mouth. I quit.

"So I just can't go then," I said.

"No," Pete said. "You just can't go. You're too little, in the first place, and in the second place —"

"All right," I said. "Then shut up and leave me go to sleep."

So he hushed then and laid back. And I laid there like I was already asleep, and pretty soon he was asleep and I knowed it was the wanting to go to the war that had worried him and kept him awake, and now that he had decided to go he wasn't worried any more.

The next morning he told Maw and Pap. Maw was all right. She cried.

"No," she said, crying, "I don't want him to go. I would rather go myself in his place, if I could. I don't want to save the country. Them Japanese could take it and keep it, so long as they left me and my family and my children alone. But I remember my brother Marsh in that other war. He had to go to that one when he wasn't but nineteen, and our mother couldn't understand it then any more than I can now. But she told Marsh if he had to go, he had to go. And so, if Pete's got to go to this one, he's got to go to it. Jest don't ask me to understand why."

But Pap was the one. He was the feller. "To the war?" he said. "Why, I just don't see a bit of use in that. You ain't old enough for the draft, and the country ain't being invaded. Our President in Washington, D.C., is watching the conditions and he will notify us. Besides, in that other war your ma just mentioned, I was drafted and sent clean to Texas and was held there nigh eight months until they finally quit fighting. It seems to me that, along with your uncle Marsh, who received a actual wound on the battlefields of France, is enough for me and mine to have to do to protect the country, at least in my lifetime. Besides, what'll I do for help on the farm with you gone? It seems to me I'll get mighty far behind."

"You been behind as long as I can remember," Pete said. "Anyway, I'm going. I got to."

"Of course he's got to go," I said. "Them Japanese —"

"You hush your mouth!" Maw said, crying. "Nobody's talking to you! Go and get me a armful of wood! That's what you can do!"

So I got the wood. And all the next day, while me and Pete and Pap was getting in as much wood as we could in that time because Pete said how Pap's idea of plenty of wood was one more stick laying against the wall that Maw ain't put on the fire yet, Maw was getting Pete ready to go. She washed and mended his clothes and cooked him a shoe box of vittles. And that night me and Pete laid in the bed and listened to her packing his grip and crying, until after a while Pete got up in his nightshirt and went back there, and I could hear them talking, until at last Maw said, "You got to go, and so I want you to go. But I don't understand it, and I won't never, and so don't expect me to." And Pete come back and got into the bed again and laid again still and hard as iron on his back, and then he said, and he wasn't talking to me, he wasn't talking to nobody: "I got to go. I just got to."

"Sho' you got to," I said. "Them Japanese —" He turned over hard, he kind of surged over onto his side, looking at me in the dark.

"Anyway, you're all right," he said. "I expected to have more trouble with you than with all the rest of them put together."

"I reckon I can't help it neither," I said. "But maybe it will run a few years longer and I can get there. Maybe someday I will jest walk in on you."

"I hope not," Pete said. "Folks don't go to wars for fun. A man don't leave his maw crying just for fun."

"Then why are you going?" I said.

"I got to," he said. "I just got to. Now you go on to sleep. I got to ketch that early bus in the morning."

"All right," I said. "I hear tell Memphis is a big place. How will you find where the Army's at?"

"I'll ask somebody where to go to join it," Pete said. "Go on to sleep now."

"Is that what you'll ask for? Where to join the
Army?" I said.

"Yes," Pete said. He turned onto his back again.
"Shut up and go to sleep."

We went to sleep. The next morning we et breakfast by lamplight because the bus would pass at six
o'clock. Maw wasn't crying now. She jest looked
grim and busy, putting breakfast on the table while
we et it. Then she finished packing Pete's grip, except he never wanted to take no grip to the war, but
Maw said decent folks never went nowhere, not even
to a war, without a change of clothes and something
to tote them in. She put in the shoe box of fried
chicken and biscuits and she put the Bible in, too,
and then it was time to go. We didn't know until
then that Maw wasn't going to the bus. She jest
brought Pete's cap and overcoat, and still she didn't
cry no more, she jest stood with her hands on Pete's
shoulders and she didn't move, but somehow, and
just holding Pete's shoulders, she looked as hard
and fierce as when Pete had turned toward me in
the bed last night and tole me that anyway I was
all right.

"They could take the country and keep the
country, so long as they never bothered me and
mine," she said. Then she said, "Don't never forget
who you are. You ain't rich and the rest of the world

outside of Frenchman's Bend never heard of you. But your blood is good as any blood anywhere, and don't you never forget it."

Then she kissed him, and then we was out of the house, with Pap toting Pete's grip whether Pete wanted him to or not. There wasn't no dawn even yet, not even after we had stood on the highway by the mailbox awhile. Then we seen the lights of the bus coming and I was watching the bus until it come up and Pete flagged it, and then, sho' enough, there was daylight — it had started while I wasn't watching. And now me and Pete expected Pap to say something else foolish, like he done before, about how Uncle Marsh getting wounded in France and that trip to Texas Pap had taken in 1918 ought to be enough to save the Unity States in 1942, but he never. He done all right too. He jest said, "Good-by, son. Always remember what your ma told you and write her whenever you find the time."

Then he shaken Pete's hand, and Pete looked at me a minute and put his hand on my head and rubbed my head durn nigh hard enough to wring my neck off and jumped into the bus, and the feller wound the door shut and the bus begun to hum; then it was moving, humming and grinding and whining louder and louder; it was going fast, with two little red lights behind it that never seemed to get no littler, but jest seemed to be running together until pretty soon they would touch and jest be one light. But they never did, and then the bus was gone, and even like it was, I could have pretty nigh busted out crying, nigh to nine years old and all.

Me and Pap went back to the house. All that day we worked at the wood tree, and so I never had no good chance until about the middle of the afternoon. Then I taken my slingshot and I would have like to took all my bird eggs, too, because Pete had give me his collection and he holp me with mine, and he would like to git the box out and look at them as good as I would, even if he was nigh twenty years old. But the box was too big to tote a long ways and have to worry with, so I just taken the shikepoke egg, because it was the best un, and wropped it up good into a matchbox and hid it and the slingshot under the corner of the barn. Then we et supper and went to bed, and I thought then how if I woulda had to stayed in that room and that bed like that even for one more night I jest couldn't-a stood it. Then I could hear Pap snoring, but I never heard no sound from Maw, whether she was asleep or not, and I don't reckon she was. So I taken my shoes and drapped them out the window, and then I clumb out like I used to watch Pete do when he was still jest seventeen and Pap held that he was too young yet to be tomcatting around at night, and wouldn't leave him out, and I put on my shoes and went to the barn and got the slingshot and the shike-poke egg and went to the highway.

It wasn't cold, it was jest durn confounded dark, and that highway stretched on in front of me like, without nobody using it, it had stretched out half again as fer jest like a man does when he lays down, so that for a time it looked like full sun was going to ketch me before I had finished them twenty-two miles to Jefferson. But it didn't. Daybreak was just starting when I walked up the hill into town. I could smell breakfast cooking in the cabins and I wished I had thought to brought me a cold biscuit, but that was too late now. And Pete had told me Memphis was a piece beyond Jefferson, but I never knowed it was no eighty miles. So I stood there on that empty square, with daylight coming and coming and the street lights still burning and that law looking down at me, and me still eighty miles from Memphis, and it had took me all night to walk jest twenty-two miles, and so, by the time I got to Memphis at that rate, Pete would-a done already started for Pearl Harbor.

"Where do you come from?" the law said.

And I told him again. "I got to git to Memphis. My brother's there."

"You mean you ain't got any folks around here?" the law said. "Nobody but that brother? What are you doing way off down here and your brother in Memphis?"

And I told him again, "I got to git to Memphis. I ain't got no time to waste talking about it and I ain't got time to walk it. I got to git there today."

"Come on here," the law said.

We went down another street. And there was the bus, jest like when Pete got into it yestiddy morning, except there wasn't no lights on it now and it was empty. There was a regular bus deepo like a railroad deepo, with a ticket counter and a feller behind it, and the law said, "Set down over there," and I set down on the bench, and the law said, "I want to use your telephone," and he talked in the telephone a minute and put it down and said to the feller behind the ticket counter, "Keep your eye on him. I'll be back as soon as Mrs. Habersham can arrange to get herself up and dressed." He went out. I got up and went to the ticket counter.

"I want to go to Memphis," I said.

"You bet," the feller said. "You set down on the bench now. Mr. Foote will be back in a minute."

"I don't know no Mr. Foote," I said. "I want to ride that bus to Memphis."

"You got some money?" he said. "It'll cost you seventy-two cents."

I taken out the matchbox and unwropped the shikepoke egg." I'll swap you this for a ticket to Memphis," I said.

"What's that?" he said.

"It's a shikepoke egg," I said. "You never seen one before. It's worth a dollar. I'll take seventy-two cents fer it."

"No," he said, "the fellers that own that bus insist on a cash basis. If I started swapping tickets for bird eggs and livestock and such, they would fire me. You go and set down on the bench now, like Mr. Foote —"

I started for the door, but he caught me; he put one hand on the ticket counter and jumped over it and caught up with me and reached his hand out to ketch my shirt. I whupped out my pocketknife and snapped it open.

"You put a hand on me and I'll cut it off," I said.

I tried to dodge him and run at the door, but he could move quicker than any grown man I ever see, quick as Pete almost. He cut me off and stood with his back against the door and one foot raised a little, and there wasn't no other way to get out.

"Get back on that bench and stay there," he said.

And there wasn't no other way out. And he stood there with his back against the door. So I went back to the bench. And then it seemed like to me that deepo was full of folks. There was that law again, and there was two ladies in fur coats and their faces already painted. But they still looked like they had got up in a hurry and they still never liked it, a old one and a young one, looking down at me.

"He hasn't got a overcoat!" the old one said. "How in the world did he ever get down here by himself?"

"I ask you," the law said. "I couldn't get nothing out of him except his brother is in Memphis and he wants to get back up there."

"That's right," I said. "I got to git to Memphis today."

"Of course you must," the old one said. "Are you sure you can find your brother when you get to Memphis?"

"I reckon I can," I said. "I ain't got but one and I have knowed him all my life. I reckon I will know him again when I see him."

The old one looked at me. "Somehow he doesn't look like he lives in Memphis," she said.

"He probably don't," the law said. "You can't tell though. He might live anywhere, overhalls or

not. This day and time they get scattered over-
night from he-hope to breakfast; boys and girls,
too, almost before they can walk good. He might
have been in Missouri or Texas yestiddy, for all we
know. But he don't seem to have any doubt his
brother is in Memphis. All I know to do is send him
up there and leave him look."

"Yes," the old one said.

The young one set down on the bench by me and
opened a hand satchel and taken out a artermatic
writing pen and some papers.

"Now, honey," the old one said, "we're going to
see that you find your brother, but we must have a
case history for our files first. We want to know your
name and your brother's name and where you were
born and when your parents died."

"I don't need no case history neither," I said. "All
I want is to get to Memphis. I got to git there
today."

"You see?" the law said. He said it almost like he
enjoyed it. "That's what I told you."

"You're lucky, at that, Mrs. Habersham," the bus
feller said. "I don't think he's got a gun on him,
but he can open that knife da — I mean, fast enough
to suit any man."

But the old one just stood there looking at me.

"Well," she said. "Well. I really don't know what to do."

"I do," the bus feller said. "I'm going to give him a ticket out of my own pocket, as a measure of protecting the company against riot and bloodshed. And when Mr. Foote tells the city board about it, it will be a civic matter and they will not only reimburse me, they will give me a medal too. Hey, Mr. Foote?"

But never nobody paid him no mind. The old one still stood looking down at me. She said, "Well," again. Then she taken a dollar from her purse and give it to the buss feller. "I suppose he will travel on a child's ticket, won't he?"

"Wellum," the bus feller said, "I just don't know what the regulations would be. Likely I will be fired for not crating him and marking the crate Poison. But I'll risk it."

Then they were gone. Then the law came back with a sandwich and give it to me.

"You're sure you can find that brother?" he said.

"I ain't yet convinced why not," I said. "If I don't see Pete first, he'll see me. He knows me too."

Then the law went out for good, too, and I et the sandwich. Then more folks come in and bought tickets, and then the bus feller said it was time to go, and I got into the bus just like Pete done, and we was gone.

I seen all the towns. I seen all of them. When the bus got to going good I found out I was jest about wore out for sleep. But there was too much I hadn't never saw before. We run out of Jefferson and run past fields and woods, then we would run into another town and out of that un and past fields and woods again, and then into another town with stores and gins and water tanks, and we run along by the railroad for a spell and I seen the signal arm move, and then I seen the train and then some more towns, and I was jest about plumb wore out for sleep, but I couldn't resk it. Then Memphis begun. It seemed like, to me, it went on for miles. We would pass a patch of stores and I would think that was sho'ly it and the bus would even stop. But it wouldn't be Memphis yet and we would go on again past water tanks and smokestacks on top of the mills, and if they was gins and sawmills, I never knowed there was that many and I never seen any that big, and where they got enough cotton and logs to run 'um I don't know.

Then I seen Memphis, I knowed I was right this time. It was standing up into the air. It looked like about a dozen whole towns bigger than Jefferson was set up on one edge in a field, standing up into

the air higher than ara hill in all Yoknapatawpha
County. Then we was in it, with the bus stopping
ever' few feet, it seemed like to me, and cars rushing
past on both sides of it and the streets crowded with
folks from ever'where in town that day, until I didn't
see how there could-a been nobody left in Mis'sippi
a-tall to even sell a bus ticket, let alone write out
no case histories. Then the bus stopped. It was
another bus deepo, a heap bigger than the one in
Jefferson. And I said, "All right. Where do folks
join the Army?"

"What?" the bus feller said.

And I said it again, "Where do folks join the
Army?"

"Oh," he said. Then he told me how to get there.
I was afraid at first I wouldn't ketch on how to do
in a town big as Memphis. But I caught on all
right. I never had to ask but twice more. Then I
was there, and I was durn glad to git out of all them
rushing cars and shoving folks and all that racket
for a spell, and I thought, It won't be long now, and
I thought how if there was any kind of a crowd
there that had done already joined the Army, too,
Peter would likely see me before I seen him. And
so I walked into the room. And Pete wasn't there.

He wasn't even there. There was a soldier with a
big arrerhead on his sleeve, writing, and two fellers

standing in front of him, and there was some more folks there, I reckon. It seems to me I remember some more folks there.

I went to the table where the soldier was writing, and I said," Where's Pete?" and he looked up and I said, "My brother. Pete Grier. Where is he?"

"What?" the soldier said. "Who?"

And I told him again. "He joined the Army yestiddy. He's going to Pearl Harbor. So am I. I want to ketch him. Where you-all got him?" Now they were all looking at me, but I never paid them no mind. "Come on," I said. "Where is he?"

The soldier had quit writing. He had both hands spraddled out on the table. "Oh," he said. "You're going, too, hah?"

"Yes," I said. "They got to have wood and water. I can chop it and tote it. Come on. Where's Pete?"

The soldier stood up. "Who let you in here?" he said. "Go on. Beat it."

"Durn that," I said. "You tell me where Pete —"

I be dog if he couldn't move faster than the bus feller even. He never come over the table, he come around it, he was on me almost before I knowed it, so that I jest had time to jump back and whup out my pocketknife and snap it open and hit one lick, and he hollered and jumped back and grabbed one hand with the other and stood there cussing and hollering.

One of the other fellers grabbed me from behind, and I hit at him with the knife, but I couldn't reach him.

Then both of the fellers had me from behind, and then another soldier come out of a door at the back. He had on a belt with a britching strop over one shoulder.

"What the hell is this?" he said.

"That little son cut me with a knife!" the first soldier hollered. When he said that I tried to git at him again, but both them fellers was holding me, two against one, and the soldier with the backing strop said, "Here, here. Put your knife up, feller. None of us are armed. A man don't knife-fight folks that are barehanded." I could begin to hear him then. He sounded jest like Pete talked to me. "Let him go," he said. They let me go. "Now what's all the trouble about?" And I told him. "I see," he said. "And you come up to see if he was all right before he left."

"No," I said. "I came to —"

But he had already turned to where the first soldier was wropping a handkerchief around his hand.

"Have you got him?" he said. The first soldier went back to the table and looked at some papers.

"Here he is," he said. "He enlisted yestiddy. He's in a detachment leaving this morning for Little Rock." He had a watch stropped on his arm. He looked at it. "The train leaves in about fifty minutes. If I know country boys, they're probably all down there at the station right now."

"Get him up here," the one with the backing strop said. "Phone the station. Tell the porter to get him a cab. And you come with me," he said.

It was another office behind that un, with jest a table and some chairs. We set there while the soldier smoked, and it wasn't long; I knowed Pete's feet soon as I heard them. Then the first soldier opened the door and Pete come in. He never had no soldier clothes on. He looked jest like he did when he got on the bus yestiddy morning, except it seemed to me like it was at least a week, so much had happened, and I had done had to do so much traveling. He come in and there he was, looking at me like he hadn't never left home, except that here we was in Memphis, on the way to Pearl Harbor.

"What in durnation are you doing here?" he said.

And I told him, "You got to have wood and water to cook with. I can chop it and tote it for you-all."

"No," Pete said. "You're going back home."

"No, Pete," I said. "I got to go too. I got to. It hurts my heart, Pete."

"No," Pete said. He looked at the soldier. "I jest don't know what could have happened to him, Lootenant," he said. "He never drawed a knife on anybody before in his life." He looked at me. "What did you do it for?"

"I don't know," I said. "I jest had to. I jest had to git here. I jest had to find you."

"Well, don't you never do it again, you hear?" Pete said. "You put that knife in your pocket and you keep it there. If I ever again hear of you drawing it on anybody, I'm coming back from wherever I am at and whup the fire out of you. You hear me?"

"I would sure cut a throat if it would bring you back to stay," I said. "Pete," I said. "Pete."

"No," Pete said. Now his voice wasn't hard and quick no more, it was almost quiet, and I knowed now I wouldn't never change him. "You must go home. You must look after Maw, and I am depending on you to look after my ten acres. I want you to go back home. Today. Do you hear?"

"I hear," I said.

"Can he get back home by himself?" the soldier said.

"He come up here by himself," Pete said.

"I can get back, I reckon," I said. "I don't live in but one place. I don't reckon it's moved."

Pete taken a dollar out of his pocket and give it to me. "That'll buy your bus ticket right to our mailbox," he said. "I want you to mind the lootenant. He'll send you to the bus. And you go back home and you take care of Maw and look after my ten acres and keep that durn knife in your pocket. You hear me?"

"Yes, Pete," I said.

"All right," Pete said. "Now I got to go." He put his hand on my head again. But this time he never wrung my neck. He just laid his hand on my head a minute. And then I be dog if he didn't lean down and kiss me, and I heard his feet and then the door, and I never looked up and that was all, me setting there, rubbing the place where Pete kissed me and the soldier throwed back in his chair, looking out the window and coughing. He reached into his pocket and handed something to me without looking around. It was a piece of chewing gum.

"Much obliged," I said. "Well, I reckon I might as well start back. I got a right fer piece to go."

"Wait," the soldier said. Then he telephoned again and I said again I better start back, and he said again, "Wait. Remember what Pete told you."

So we waited, and then another lady come in,

old, too, in a fur coat, too, but she smelled all right, she never had no artermatic writing pen nor no case history either. She come in and the soldier got up, and she looked around quick until she saw me, and come and put her hand on my shoulder light and quick and easy as Maw herself might-a done it.

"Come on," she said. "Let's go home to dinner."

"Nome," I said. "I got to ketch the bus to Jefferson."

"I know. There's plenty of time. We'll go home and eat dinner first."

She had a car. And now we was right down in the middle of them other cars. We was almost under the busses, and all them crowds of people on the street close enough to where I could have talked to them if I had knowed who they was. After a while she stopped the car. "Here we are," she said, and I looked at it, and if all that was her house, she sho' had a big family. But all of it wasn't. We crossed a hall with trees growing in it and went into a little room without nothing in it but a nigger dressed up in a uniform a heap shinier than them soldiers had, and the nigger shut the door, and then I hollered, "Look out!" and grabbed, but it was all right; that whole little room jest went right on up and stopped and the door opened and we was in another hall, and the lady unlocked a door and we went in, and there was another soldier, a old feller, with a britching strop, too, and a silver-colored bird on each shoulder.

"Here we are," the lady said. "This is Colonel McKellogg. Now what would you like for dinner?"

"I reckon I'll jest have some ham and eggs and coffee," I said.

She had done started to pick up the telephone. She stopped. "Coffee?" she said. "When did you start drinking coffee?"

"I don't know," I said. "I reckon it was before I could remember."

"You're about eight, aren't you?" she said.

"Nome," I said. "I'm eight and ten months. Going on eleven months."

She telephoned then. Then we set there and I told them how Pete had jest left that morning for Pearl Harbor and I had aimed to go with him, but I would have to go back home to take care of Maw and look after Pete's ten acres, and she said how they had a little boy about my size, too, in a school in the East. Then a nigger, another one, in a short kind of shirttail coat, rolled a kind of wheelbarrer in. It had my ham and eggs and a glass of milk and a piece of pie, too, and I thought I was hungry. But when I taken the first bite I found out I couldn't swallow it, and I got up quick.

"I got to go," I said.

"Wait," she said.

"I got to go," I said.

"Just a minute," she said. "I've already telephoned for the car. It won't be but a minute now. Can't you drink the milk even? Or maybe some of your coffee?"

"Nome," I said. "I ain't hungry. I'll eat when I git home." Then the telephone rung. She never even answered it.

"There," she said. "There's the car." And we went back down in that 'ere little moving room with the dressed-up nigger. This time it was a big car with a soldier driving it. I got into the front with him. She give the soldier a dollar. "He might get hungry," she said. "Try to find a decent place for him."

"Okay, Mrs. McKellogg," the soldier said.

Then we was gone again. And now I could see Memphis good, bright in the sunshine, while we was swinging around it. And first thing I knowed, we was back on the same highway the bus run on this morning — the patches of stores and them big gins and sawmills, and Memphis running on for miles, it seemed like to me, before it begun to give out. Then we was running again between the fields and woods, running fast now, and except for that soldier, it was like I hadn't never been to Memphis a-tall. We was going fast now. At this rate, before I knowed it we would be home again, and I thought about me riding up to Frenchman's Bend in this here big car with a soldier running it, and all of a sudden I begun to cry. I never knowed I was fixing to, and I couldn't stop it. I set there by that soldier, crying. We was going fast.

IN THE
KOREAN WAR
1950-1953

From

Commander-in-Chief Harry S. Truman

"The American people, together with other free peoples, seek a new era in world affairs. We seek a world where all men may live in peace and freedom, with steadily improving living conditions, under governments of their own free choice . . . We will follow the course we have chosen with courage and with faith, because we carry in our hearts the flame of freedom. We are fighting for liberty and for peace — and with God's blessing we shall succeed."

Spoken on July 19, 1950, by President Truman in his war message to Congress

Star over Korea

by William Chamberlain

The wind was beginning to come up in the late afternoon, slapping spiteful little waves against the thin skin of the LCVP — Land Craft, Vehicles and Personnel — which bobbed up and down on the gray water a hundred yards from the island. It was a bleak-looking island — the same as any other of the many islands which dotted the sea off the southern coast of Korea. Craggy and covered with dun scrub, and lonesome in the dying December day.

It was a little different from the hundred other islands today, though, because a South Korean fisherman — coming into Pusan greatly frightened the day before — had reported that seven very tough men had landed on the island in a sampan. They would be, so the Army surmised, the seven Red PW's who had escaped from the stockade on the Big Island a week ago. North Koreans and very tough indeed.

So the Army had sent a sergeant with a detail of men, also very tough, to comb the island and bring them in. The Navy had lent an LCVP — which is very handy for landing on beaches when it is necessary to land on beaches — and three men to run it. The fact that tomorrow would be Christmas wasn't even considered by anybody. You just didn't let Red PW's run around loose, even on Christmas Eve.

Now the three men that the Navy had lent sat in the LCVP a hundred yards offshore and wished that the sergeant and his detail would hurry up and come back so that they could all go home. There had been talk of turkey and other fixings for tomorrow. After all, if the Red PW's wanted to wander around on some condemned island like this it was no skin off anybody's back but their own.

The skipper of the LCVP was a boatswain's mate, second class, named Eddie Norton. He was twenty-two and sober-minded, and much sun had burned his hair to the color of new straw. He had been in the Navy for three years now and things worried him. Things like those dark clouds climbing out of the sea in the west and the freshening wind which was beginning to kick up little whitecaps here and there. Things like the fact it would soon be dark and it was a long way home.

Kirby Dodd — who was his motor mach and who

hailed from Texas — yelled back from where he sat
on the deck playing gin runny with Seaman Czernovich. "Hey, skippeh, when we goin' home? Any
time now will suit ole Kirb, seh."

"How do I know when we're going home?" Norton asked crossly. "When that condemned sergeant
gets back with his PW's. You want me to go off and
leave him?"

"Shuah," Kirby said cheerfully. "I ain't lost no
sergeants."

That was just the trouble, Eddie Norton thought
resentfully. Everybody left everything up to him.
The so-and-so Army could go wandering around
all over hell's half acre — picking daisies, for all that
he knew — until it was dark, and then they'd come
bumbling back to the beach and bellyache at him
if he didn't get them home dry and safe. Kirb and
Czernovich could sit there on the deck and play
gin rummy and worry about nothing. Just leave
everything up to Eddie Norton. That was the idea.
Eddie was a good guy!

They didn't have to worry about those clouds
which were getting blacker over there on the horizon, and they didn't have to worry about the wind
which was beginning to kick up a sea. Let Eddie
worry about that. Good old Eddie! He had nothing
else to do.

Already the mainland was beginning to dim in the late-afternoon haze, and that depressed him further. He had had this bucket out at night before, but always for short runs along the coast. Never for a twenty-mile run across open sea with a storm beginning to show its teeth. A sudden thought struck him and he screwed himself around from his seat on the engine hatch to look at his motor mach again.

"You put that compass in the locker like I told you?" he asked, his voice sharp.

Kirby looked up, startled. "Well, what do you know?" he said with a faint note of apology in his voice. "I reckon I jest plumb forgot that daggone thing, skippeh."

"What!"

"Yeah," Kirby said mournfully. "I was goin' to get it an' then Ensign Thompson stops me to ask about them new injectors an' I guess I jest plumb forgot it."

"You're a big help," Norton told him bitterly. "I don't know why I don't run this can by myself. I'd be better off if I did."

He lapsed into morose silence while he braced his feet against the gunwhale and wrapped his arms moodily about his knees. The wind was getting stronger all the time now, he thought as he shivered

a little. Cold too. It cut right through his jacket.
Well, why shouldn't it be cold? It was December
twenty-fourth. Christmas Eve — now that was a
laugh! He ought to hang up his stocking! He looked
at his watch and it was a quarter after four — that
sergeant should have been back long ago.

A sampan, beating north against the wind, passed
a hundred yards away and he turned his head to
watch it. Gook in it, and a gook woman, and a
couple of gook kids. Probably a pig and a crateful
of chickens, too, he thought. The voices of his crew
reached him faintly as they bent over their gin
game.

"You know what I'm goin' to do when I get back
to Texas, pappy?" Kirby was saying.

"Get married an' raise thee keed," Czernovich
said.

"Nope," Kirby told him. "Us Dodds is the
bachelor type. I'm goin' to get me a red automobile with white wheels an' then I'm goin' to train
that there automobile."

"W'at you mean — train heem?"

"Jest what I said, pappy, seh. I'm goin' to train
that daggone automobile so does it get within a half
mile of so much wateh as you could wash yoah face
in, it runs to beat hell."

"W'at you do that for, keed?"

"So's ole Kirb doan eveh see no moah of this daggone Navy, pappy. That's why. Guess maybe I shouldn't ought to have forgot that daggone compass, at that. Maybe we're goin' to need it."

"W'at for?" Czernovich asked. "Don' we know where we're going without thee compass?"

Kirby gave him a bright, irritated glance. "We know wheah we're goin' all right, but maybe we doan know how to get there once it gets good and dark."

"Then we use thee star," Czernovich said calmly. "Joost thee same as thee three wise men, eh?"

"I wouldn't know about no wise men," Kirby said.

"I am hear about them when I am thee leetle keed," Czernovich said. "My mamma ees tell me. They are follow thee star on Chreestmas Eve to see thee baby. So, we are follow thee star too."

"Seh," Kirby said, "you could say that we got three men on this heah tub all right. To say they was three wise men would be stretchin' a point. Let's knock it off, pappy. I got to go comfort Eddie. He feels bad about that compass that we ain't got."

He climbed to his feet and made his way aft to where Norton still sat on the engine hatch staring gloomily at the clouds, which were getting blacker in the west.

"I shore am sorry about that theah compass,

Eddie," he said. "Do you want to kick my tail, I'll bend oveh."

"Skip it," Norton told him. "Maybe we won't need it anyway." A faint hail from the beach drifted out to them and he brightened as he swung around. "There's Sergeant Waggoner now, I guess."

It wasn't though. It was just one man who stood there in the fading light, beckoning them in. Norton scowled as he kicked the engine over and swung the bow of the LCVP in toward the beach. One man there could mean trouble, he thought anxiously. He glanced back over his shoulder to look again at those threatening clouds.

The beach was steeply sloping and he ran the LCVP in hard; jazzed the engine to hold it there while Czernovich dropped the ramp and the soldier scrambled aboard.

"Where's Waggoner and the rest?" he yelled at the man as Czernovich began to crank up the ramp again.

The soldier came aft — corporal about his own age, Norton saw, with an M-1 slung over his shoulder and a grenade hanging on his chest. "He won't be here for maybe an hour yet," the corporal said. "He sent me to tell you."

Norton scowled at that. Czernovich yelled from the bow that the ramp was secure, and he backed the engine and they pulled off the beach again. They got clear and clawed their way back to deep water and Norton turned his attention back to the soldier.

"Why won't he be here for an hour?" he demanded angrily. "Can't he see that it's getting dark and there's a storm making up? I should think that even a sergeant could see that!"

"He can see it all right, Mac," the corporal said. "Only he can't do nothing about it. McClosky busted his leg over across the island and they got to carry him."

"My, my," Kirby said from across the engine hatch. "Busted his laig, huh? It jest goes to show that walkin' ain't safe."

"It's the guys doin' the walking that are the guys winning the war over here, Mac," the corporal said.

"Wah!" Kirby said in a shocked voice. "This heah ain't no wah. It's a police action. Ain't you heard?"

"Maybe it's a police action to you guys riding around in your nice, comfortable little boats — sleepin' in, and with ice cream twice a day," the corporal said roughly. The old-young look deepened in his face. "It ain't no police action to us guys squattin' in foxholes."

"Break it up," Norton said tiredly. "What dif-
ference does it make what it is as long as you're
cold and wet and there's a storm making up?"

It was six o'clock and the December day had
faded into a cheerless dusk as Norton looked at his
watch for the fiftieth time. A rain squall, sweeping
out of the west, had left the four of them soaked
and shivering in the wind which still grew. Then
the hail for which Norton had been waiting came
from the beach, and he saw the slender file of men
which wound out of the scrub.

"It's Waggoner," the corporal said, coming up
beside the engine hatch. "McClosky's leg is messed
up bad — bone sticking out. They had to take it
easy with him."

Norton nodded and kicked the engine over and
they headed for the beach again. Maybe there was
still daylight enough left for them to make it back
to the base O.K., he thought. Deep in his heart he
knew that there wasn't, though, and the knowledge
made a cold little knot in the pit of his stomach.

The LCVP slammed into the shingle and the
rollers were running higher there now so that he
had to jazz the engine constantly to hold the boat
up there. The ramp went down with a splash and
men began to come aboard, jumping precariously

as the LCVP heaved up and down. Sergeant Waggoner's voice lifted hoarsely.

"Easy with him there! For crying out loud, take it easy! You ain't loadin' ammunition boxes!"

They passed McClosky in, quick hands reaching for him, and then Sergeant Waggoner waved a thick arm. "That's all of us, Navy!" he shouted against the wind. "Let's get out!"

Norton heard the clank of the dogs as Czernovich wound up the ramp, and he shoved the lever into reverse and gunned the engine and they began to pull away from the shore again. A big roller surged under the stern of the landing craft, lifting it high, and for a moment Norton seemed to be peering down at the beach from a vast height.

For a short, panicky second, he thought they were going to broach, but they didn't.

He opened the throttle wide and felt the propeller bite greedily at the water and then they began to make sternway and were drawing clear. A hundred yards out he turned and the trough, as they fell off into it for a moment, was steeply dangerous. The sea had built up a lot in the last fifteen minutes, he thought anxiously as he squinted through the gathering darkness and put the LCVP on a quartering course for the mainland which loomed dimly twenty miles away. An island, bigger than the rest, marked the halfway point and they would pass it close to starboard. A guide, of sorts, if the light gave out too soon.

They came out from behind the lee of the island which had sheltered them during the afternoon and the full force of the wind hit them now. The waves were bigger here and the quartering course which they had to take racked the LCVP with violent hands. Sergeant Waggoner came aft to hang onto the rail while he shouted at Norton.

"Couldn't make it no sooner," he yelled. "Mc-Closky fell off a cliff and busted his leg. Too bad he didn't fall on his head, the slue-footed dummy!"

Sergeant Waggoner's voice bore no malice, but there was a faint apprehension in it, the apprehension of a man who is unaccustomed to deep waters and who fears them as being something unknown and therefore darkly dangerous. Norton braced himself and eased the wheel to meet a wave which thundered out of the gloom.

"Yeah," he said. "The corporal told me. You find those gooks you were looking for?"

The sergeant shook his head. "They'd been there all right. We found signs of 'em, but they ain't there now."

"Where you suppose they went?"

"I don't know an' I don't care," Sergeant Waggoner said flatly. "It's blowin' up to storm, ain't it?"

"Just a little blow, maybe," Norton answered. He hadn't missed that note of concern in the sergeant's voice. He glanced back over his shoulder at the heavy clouds which blotted out the horizon to the west, and thought sourly that the other had just cause to worry. He couldn't let the Army know that, though. "Just a little squall."

"You think we can get back O.K.?"

"Sure, we'll get back."

"I don't like water," Sergeant Waggoner said with sudden violence. "I don't even like water to wash my face in! An' I didn't come to this war to go sailin' around on the water either!"

Kirby, from the other side of the engine hatch, made clicking little sounds with his tongue. "Think of that!" he said. "I sweah, suh, I wouldn't neveh have guessed it. You look like the web-footed type to me. You look right down amphibious."

The sergeant gave him an angry glance. "I could do without the Navy too," he said. "That dumb McClosky! Two years up in the lines an' he never gets a scratch. Then he comes down here an' has to break his fool leg and hold us up until dark!"

"He hurt bad?" Norton asked.

"Yeah, bad. The bone's stickin' out — an' this

bouncing all around ain't doin' him no good, either."

Kirby said, his voice suddenly deadly serious, "This heah bouncin' around that we're gettin' now ain't nothin' to what's comin', Army. Look back theah, Eddie!"

Norton looked back over his shoulder again and his lips were pressed more tightly together when he swung back again to scowl into the gloom. He had seen the white line on the water a couple of thousand yards astern and he knew what was coming. A squall and a good one!

It hit five minutes later and blotted out the seas on either side in a smother of slashing rain and howling wind. Visibility went down to zero and the flying spray drove against the back of Norton's neck like slung bird shot. The stern of the LCVP yawed violently and Norton held his course blindly by feel alone.

Czernovich came aft to crouch down beside Kirby in the shelter of the engine hatch. Forward, Norton could dimly make out the shapes of the soldiers as they huddled, heads below the gunwales, and tried to keep the injured man steady. This couldn't last, Norton thought. It was just a squall. It'd be over in a couple of minutes.

It wasn't though. The minutes built up into five;

grew to ten, and still the wind screamed eerily across the water and the seas built up higher and higher. One, bigger than the rest, overtook the laboring LCVP and he felt the heavy slam of water against his legs as it came aboard. The steady throb of the engine took on a deeper tone for a moment, then coughed hoarsely and quit. The sudden quietness was like an unexpected blow across the face.

"Ah-h-h, the she-devil!" Kirby said in a shocked voice which carried above the wind. "The dirty she-devil!"

He was on his knees, yanking the engine cover off. Czernovich crawled away in the gloom, came back, and the bright beam of a flashlight splashed across the hatch. In its glare, Norton could see Kirby's face — good humor gone now, to leave it thin-lipped and grim — as the Texan worked with swift, frantic hands. In his own hands, the wheel twisted back and forth uselessly.

"What is it Kirb?" he called out. That did no good, he knew. It was just something to say.

"Injector, I think," the motor mach yelled back at him. "I hate engines! I wisht I had a horse!"

The rain stopped, but the wind was getting worse. It had shifted around to the north, Norton thought. He couldn't be sure of that — they were drifting every which way. They fell off into a trough and rolled the port gunwhale almost under. That's the way it would be, Norton knew, until finally a big enough trough came along and then they would roll all the way over and that would be the end of the war. He felt sorry for that guy back there with the broken leg.

Then Kirby yelled, "Try her, Eddie!" and he did, and the engine caught and settled down to a sputtering roar. A ragged cadence, not like the smooth sound of power that should be there, but better than nothing. A lot better than nothing.

"Best I can do now, Eddie," Kirby yelled again. "Better go ahead an' try her with what we've got!"

Norton swung the wheel, felt the rudder bite slowly; and then the LCVP crawled limpingly back until she was quartering the seas again. Quartering which way? Norton wondered. He was turned around; completely turned around. If he only had that compass! For all that he knew now, they might be heading squarely out to sea. The thought tightened that cold knot in his stomach.

The violence of the wind died away slowly and he knew that the squall had passed. Another would come, though. He'd seen two winters here in Korea; seen enough to know that that squall would be no isolated incident at this time of year. After a while it would really start to blow.

They went on for three quarters of an hour, blackness now lying like an old woman's shawl on the sea around them. Sergeant Waggoner came crawling aft again and his voice was worried and uncertain.

"We almost there, skipper?" he asked.

"Yeah," Norton told him. "Just about."

"It's a good thing," the sergeant said. "McClosky's pretty bad off." He went forward again, crawling on his hands and knees.

Across the engine hatch, Kirby said, "What you want to lie to him like that foah, Eddie?"

Anger drove a little thread through Norton. Why the devil did he have to do all this by himself? The sergeant, McClosky back there with his busted leg, Kirby, and all the rest! They just sat by and expected him to pull the bunny out of the hat. We almost there! We're almost right out in the middle of nothing, you dimwits!

"Just keep that engine going!" he snarled at Kirby.

They went on for another half hour — climbing up the near slope of a steep water mountain, sliding down the other. The engine snuffled along like an old woman. No power. No nothing — but it kept on going. Conviction that they were headed wrong began to settle heavily on Norton's shoulders. Like a felt blanket dipped in tar.

Kirby's voice came again from beyond the engine hatch. "We're lost, Eddie, ain't we?" it said tightly. "Ole Kirb'll have to take the blame foah that one. Only, maybe takin' the blame won't be enough any moah, now."

"Next time don't forget any compasses." Norton said grimly.

Czernovich, silent for the last hour, said out of the darkness, "Maybe we could guide on thee star, eh?"

Norton swore under his breath. The guy was slap happy. He was full of the spirit of Christmas Eve! He ought to be in a home for backward children. He wanted a star when the ceiling was hanging down so low that you could reach up and touch it.

"What star?" he asked violently. "Show me a star!"

"Those star over there," Czernovich said.

Dimly, Norton could see that the other was pointing to starboard and he squinted in that direction. For a moment he saw nothing; then an almost imperceptible wink of yellow came out of the murk. He thought that he must be crazy, but he waited and presently it came again to burn faintly but steadily above the water.

"Well, I'll be damned," he mumbled under his breath. "I just will be damned!"

It was no star, he knew — too low to be a star, and, besides, the clouds were too thick for a star to shine through. But it was a light, and a light could mean land. And land meant shelter from that storm which was building up again.

"Joost thee same as thee star wheech my mamma ees tell me about when I am a leetle keed," Czernovich said.

Kirby was paying no attention to him. "What you think it is, Eddie?" he was saying.

"Must be a beacon of some sort," Norton said tightly. "Whatever it is, I'm heading for it. You think that you can keep that condemned tea-kettle of yours percolating long enough to reach it?"

"That teakettle will percolate or else," Kirby said grimly.

Norton changed course until they were quartering across the seas in the opposite direction, and they went on for a half hour while the wind began to build up again and the rollers continued to grow. The LCVP battered and banged its way along, the engine stuttering perversely but still continuing to go. It had better keep going, Norton thought grimly. There was a quality to that wind on his neck that said the next blow wasn't going to be mild — it was going to be a heller.

Sergeant Waggoner came crawling aft again. He hauled himself up beside Norton and nervously worried a bite off a worn plug of tobacco. "How much longer, Mac?" he asked.

"Not long."

"It'd better not be," Waggoner said harshly. He offered the plug to Norton; put it back in his pocket when the latter shook his head. "McClosky's takin' an awful beating up there. He ain't goin' to be able to take a lot more of it."

"O.K.," Norton said.

The light was getting nearer and brighter now and he concentrated on that; tried to keep the feeble stuttering of the engine out of his ears. Kirby was crouched there, fiddling. Well, if there was anybody who could keep that fool thing going it was Kirby. He might forget compasses, but he knew his engines.

The island loomed out of the murk with a ghostly suddenness. One second there was nothing in front of them except a wall of blackness; the next, a shadowy headland was blocking the way and Norton could see a white line of surf shimmering ahead. They limped on. The light winked dead ahead and a hundred feet up. *Cliffs here*, Norton thought, and the knot in his stomach grew tighter. Even an

LCVP didn't land in breakers pounding against the rocks.

He was starting to put the wheel over — claw off again — when his straining eyes caught sight of something which made him suck his breath in deeply. There was a break in that line of boiling waves, and a break could mean that there was a passageway through and a sheltered cove behind. For a moment he hesitated, then set his lips in a hard line and drove the LCVP on.

Kirby was yelling, "Them's rocks theah, man! Pull off! Foah heaven's sake, pull off!"

Norton shook his head stubbornly and braced his feet against the deck as the wheel kicked in his hands. No going back now. Either they made it or they didn't. Not too bad a choice, as that wind was cold and wicked against his face now.

The light winked out into the night above his head and he remembered vaguely the thing that Czernovich had been saying. Maybe the light would take them in — as that star had brought three other men safely in, nearly two thousand years ago. And wasn't that a thought! How nutty could a man get!

The breakers were close on either side now. They tossed their manes like wild horses and their roar came to Norton's ears above the whine of the wind. Unseen hands were reaching for the LCVP, tossing it crazily back and forth, and the wheel seemed malignantly alive under Norton's hands. For a second the boat seemed to hang suspended in space and he thought that they were going to broach to; then they broke free again and went forward with a rush and were suddenly out of the welter of foam and into the calm water of the cove.

Norton throttled back and they drifted with bare steerageway on toward the shallow beach. He felt limp and tired. Kirby got up slowly from where he had been kneeling by the engine hatch.

"You brought us in, seh," he said in an awed voice. "You sho'ly did. From now on, ole Kirb's yoah dog — only he don't eveh want to do that again. Wheah are we, Eddie?"

Norton shook his head. "I don't know. One of the other islands, I guess. We'll stick here until daylight, then see."

Czernovich had the flashlight and he flicked it on, its thin beam stabbing ahead. There was a beach a hundred feet away; beyond that, scrub which sloped steeply upward. Then the beam picked up something else in its fringe and Czernovich moved it until it fell on a sampan riding at anchor to the left. Norton was swinging the LCVP in that direction when a faint hail came from the beach.

"Americans, please to come quick! Please to come."

"We got company," Kirby said. "Well, nothin' ain't too good for 'em in ole Kirb's book if they stuck that light up theah!"

Norton didn't answer. He was swinging the bow of the LCVP in toward the beach again and, after a moment, Czernovich's flashlight picked out the slight figure of a man who stood on the shingle and waved his arms frantically. Norton called softly to Sergeant Waggoner.

"Better cover this guy, Sarge."

"He's got five M-1's lookin' at him right now, Mac," Sergeant Waggoner answered. "Drive on."

The man was calling eagerly, "Not to be fear, Americans. Not to be fear. I am fren'."

Norton drove the LCVP hard onto the beach and the ramp went down with a clang and Sergeant Waggoner, a half-dozen men following him, charged out. Norton said, "Take the wheel, Kirb," and followed. Czernovich's light made a little circle of radiance on the beach.

There was a South Korean there — a small, wiry man with soft brown eyes and a little mustache. He was talking with Sergeant Waggoner with an apologetic eagerness as Norton joined them.

"I am so glad that you 'ave come," he was saying.

"I am see you by thee other island thees afternoon an' so I am put up thee light, no? I am hope that you weel see an' weel come."

"What's it all about?" Norton asked.

Sergeant Waggoner spat tobacco juice. "You got me, Mac." He turned back to the Korean. "Come on, Joe. What's the dope?"

The man smiled uncertainly and spread his hands. "Eet ees thee Red," he explained. "They 'ave come here an' they 'ave make my wife thee preesoner in her house, sir. They are say I mus' take them away in thee sampan or else they are beat her, sir."

"What Reds?" Sergeant Waggoner asked.

"Maybe the birds you been looking for all day," Norton said. "It could be, couldn't it?"

"It could be," Sergeant Waggoner said grimly. "Go on, Joe."

The Korean spread his hands again and his smile became more apologetic. "They mus' not beat her," he said. "You see, sirs, her time is almost upon her. So, I slip out an' feex thee light because I think that thee Americans weel come."

"Where are these birds, Joe?" Sergeant Waggoner interrupted.

The South Korean turned his head to look fearfully back into the darkness. "Een there, sirs. At my house."

"This is where I come in, Mac," Sergeant Waggoner said softly to Norton. "Come on, boys!"

Daylight came and the wind had gone down and the seas were beginning to flatten out. Five miles away, beyond the lip of the cove, lay the base, and Christmas turkey. Norton felt good as he took the wheel and kicked the engine over. Even that engine sounded better this morning — Kirby had been tinkering with it. They had resplinted McClosky's leg and he'd be all right. Seven Red PW's, trussed up and looking the worse for wear, sat on the deck of the LCVP staring sullenly at the soldiers who guarded them.

All in all, it hadn't been a bad mission.

"Where the devil is Czernovich?" he asked Kirby. "Let's get going."

"He an' the sergeant went back to say good-by to that gook," Kirby said. "They'll be along."

They came after a moment, Czernovich in the lead. The big man's moon-shaped face bore a smirk, and even Sergeant Waggoner looked pleased with himself. They climbed on board and Czernovich cranked up the ramp, the dogs clanking metallically in the cold morning. Norton pulled the LCVP off the beach and swung her and then they went on out through the break in the reef and headed for the open sea. Czernovich came back to stand beside the engine hatch.

"Where the devil were you?" Norton asked. "Aren't you interested in turkey, bub?"

"I am take thee present to thee keed," Czernovich said happily. "Thee Chreestmas present."

"Kid? What kid?"

"Thee leetle Korea keed wheech ees born las' night. I am give heem thee flashlight."

"The flashlight!" Norton yelped. "Listen, you nutty Polack, that's Navy property! What'd you give him the flashlight for?"

Czernovich grinned broadly. "Are we not thee wise men like een thee story? We mus' take thee geeft. Thee sergeant ees give heem thee tobacco to chew on when he ees get thee teeth."

From

The Charter of the United Nations

To save succeeding generations from the scourge of war . . . to practice tolerance and live together in peace and with one another as good neighbors.